"This is sheer delight for the reader, ...a a great range of short but fascinating articles; serious science but often funny. Altogether brilliant!"

Professor Euan Clarkson, FRSE

University of Edinburgh

52 THINGS
YOU SHOULD
KNOW ABOUT
PALAEONTOLOGY

EDITED BY ALEX CULLUM & ALLARD W MARTINIUS

AgileLibre

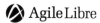
AgileLibre

First published in 2015 by Agile Libre
Nova Scotia, Canada. *www.agilelibre.com*

Technical editors Alex Cullum & Allard W Martinius
Publisher Matt Hall • *Managing editor* Kara Turner
Indexer Isabel Steurer • *Series design* electr0nika

We have done our best to ensure that the non-subjective parts of this book are factually accurate. If you find a typo or a factual inaccuracy please let us know at *hello@agilelibre.com*. While every precaution has been taken in the preparation in this book, the publisher, editors, and contributors assume no responsibility for damages resulting from the use of the information contained herein.

Front cover: Radiolarian *Actinomma antarctica*. Image by Hannes Grobe/AWI, Wikimedia Commons, licensed CC-BY.

Library and Archives Canada Cataloguing in Publication

> 52 things you should know about palaeontology / edited by
>   Alex Cullum and Allard W Martinius
> Includes bibliographical references and index.
> ISBN 978-0-9879594-4-7 (pbk.)

> 1. Paleontology. I. Cullum, Alex, 1969-, editor
> II. Martinius, Allard W, 1963-, editor
> III. Title: Fifty-two things you should know about palaeontology.

QE711.3.F53 2014   560   C2014-906759-3

*This book is dedicated to the memory of Adolf Seilacher —
one of the greatest teachers, contributors,
and motivators of our profession.*

Who we are

Agile Libre is a small independent publisher of technical books in Nova Scotia, Canada. This book is part of a series; the other two books are *52 Things You Should Know About Geophysics* and *52 Things You Should Know About Geology*. Our passion is for sharing, so our books are openly licensed and inexpensive to buy. We hope they inspire you.

Where to get this book

You will find this book for sale at *agilelibre.com*, and also at Amazon's various stores worldwide. Professors, chief geoscientists, managers, gift-givers: if you would like to buy more than 10 copies, please contact us for a discount at *hello@agilelibre.com*.

About open licenses

The contents of this book are copyright, but licensed to the world under the terms of the international Creative Commons Attribution license, which you can read about at *creativecommons.org/licenses/by/4.0*. This means you are free to share or use the contents in any way you like, provided you attribute the author of the work. We would appreciate a mention of this book as the source, too, but this is not required.

Colophon

This book was laid out on a Mac using Adobe InDesign. The cover typeface is Avant Garde Gothic and the text typefaces are Minion and Myriad. The figures were prepared in GIMP and Inkscape. It is printed and distributed through Amazon's CreateSpace publishing platform.

Contents

Alphabetical

Contents

By theme

APPLICATION
APPLIED • INTERPRETATION

TEACHING
COMMUNICATION • TEACHING

STRATIGRAPHY

BIOSTRATIGRAPHY • CHRONOLOGY

METHODS

METHODS • QUANTITATIVE

FOSSILS
COLLECTING • CURATION • FIELDWORK • PRESERVATION

CULTURE
CAREERS • COMMENT • CULTURE

Introduction

It has been an amazing journey round the globe contacting almost 200 colleagues. What has emerged from all this correspondence is a new awareness of a global discipline, that cares about discussion and communication, and is committed to pushing ahead with great enthusiasm. So many people have joined this project along the way, often submitting multiple essays, that in the end we had trouble calling time. To those still wanting to contribute, we are working on a second palaeontology volume. To those involved in this volume, thank you.

One luminary palaeontologist sadly died before being able to contribute. Professor Adolf Seilacher found this project very exciting and planned a contribution on macroevolution. Dolf's work has had a profound and long-lasting impact on many palaeontologists and opened the way to multiple lines of fundamental research, including studies on early life forms, trace fossils, the evolution of form (constructional morphology), and fauna–substrate relationships. This collection of essays is dedicated to his memory.

What's in the book? Well, the great dinosaurs still command their pride of place, but the essays we received from those in this field show how the understanding of these great beasts is advancing quickly, painting an ever clearer picture of their reign. Microscopic fauna and flora are well-represented, too. Spores, pollen, and microfossils play an important role in our modern world in everything from finding hydrocarbons to catching criminals.

While we did not set out to cover every Linnean order or class, we do have essays on a diverse set of themes, groups, and genera: From scientific tutorials to passionate storytelling, and from Proterozoic seafloor to today's beaches. How many times can a giant amphibian fossil be rediscovered through time? Why are museum collections still so important? Could there really have been a lost civilization of hominids in the Triassic, and what kind of scientifically significant specimens can you find on eBay? It's all in the book so we hope you enjoy this collection of essays.

Alex Cullum & Allard W Martinius
Norway, November 2014

A NOTE FROM THE PUBLISHER

When Alex suggested this title while we were compiling *52 Things You Should Know About Geophysics*, I wanted to do it right away. I knew it to be a substantial undertaking though, and pressed on with the next book, *52 Things You Should Know About Geology*, while Alex quietly recruited Allard as co-editor and got on with it. Between them they had contributed several essays to the previous books, so I knew they understood the brief and could communicate it to a large and passionate community that is beyond my usual tribe. It's a thrill, as always, to see the project come together, and I'm grateful to the editors for their tenacity and enthusiasm. *Tusen takk til dokke!*

From the sale of each book, we're donating £1.50 (about $2.40 at the time of writing) to The Micropalaeontological Society's Educational Trust. We hope this will play a small part in growing the discipline in Europe and beyond. The application of the science to hard problems in earth science and resource development is clear — so here's to future micropalaeontologists!

Matt Hall
Nova Scotia, November 2014

INTRODUCTION

A trace fossil primer

Dirk Knaust

Fossilized structures, which result from the activity of animals and plants in the sediment, are called trace fossils or sometimes ichnofossils. Main groups of trace fossils include burrows, tracks, trails, borings, superficial excavations, coprolites, and bite traces. The study of trace fossils and bioturbate textures, called ichnology, is traditionally subdivided into invertebrate and vertebrate ichnology, depending on the assumed trace makers.

For almost 200 years, trace fossils have been described with scientific names (ichnogenus and ichnospecies), lately following the International Code of Zoological Nomenclature (*iczn.org*). In the beginning, many trace fossils were described as plants (e.g. *Chondrites*), sponges (e.g. *Spongeliomorpha*), or corals (e.g. *Rhizocorallium*), because of their morphological similarities. Today, more than 600 invertebrate ichnogenera, and probably even more vertebrate ichnogenera, are known.

The producers of trace fossils often remain unknown or can only be assigned to higher taxonomical groups of organisms. Such interpretations are based on modern analogs, functional morphology, or experiments. Neoichnology, the study of modern traces, has shown that the same organism is capable of producing different traces — e.g. a crab can burrow into the substrate, create a superficial trackway, or leave faecal pellets. The same trace can result from the activity of different trace makers — e.g. the simple vertical shaft *Skolithos*, known to be produced by insects, spiders, crustaceans, worms, and even plant roots.

Ichnologists recognize groups of trace fossils according to the assumed behaviour of their producers (Seilacher 2007). This behavioural, or ethological, classification is interpretative and often remains uncertain, because the purpose of the producer can hardly be verified and may have been manifold. Ethological categories include domichnia (dwelling), fodinichnia (feeding), repichnia (locomotion), and pascichnia (grazing); there are many more. A more descriptive classification of trace fossils uses their characteristic morphological features (such as orientation, branching, lining, fill, symmetry, number of imprints, etc.) in a hierarchical manner (Knaust 2012).

Trace fossils and bioturbate textures have importance for palaeoenvironmental and sequence-stratigraphic interpretations, and are known to influ-

Ichnologists recognize groups of trace fossils according to the assumed behaviour of their producers.

ence the quality of hydrocarbon reservoirs and aquifers (Buatois & Mángano 2011, Knaust & Bromley 2012, Knaust 2014). There are two complementing concepts in ichnology: ichnofacies and ichnofabrics. Ichnofacies are broader depositional environments — such as shores, shelf, continental slope, and deep sea — which are characterized by particular trace-fossil associations (e.g. dominantly vertical, horizontal, or spreiten burrows). Identifying specific ichnofacies can be useful in cases where little data is available (e.g. new exploration areas). Ichnofabrics, on the other hand, contain all ichnological components of a rock (e.g. the combination of trace fossils resulting from various colonization events) and reflect their relationship with the sedimentological features (such as bedding). Thus, ichnofabric analysis becomes useful in the detailed description and interpretation of bioturbated sediments and sedimentary rocks.

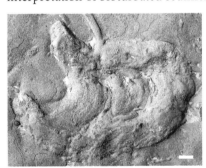 

Trace fossils on a bedding plane. Scale bars = 1 cm. Left: *Rhizocorallium commune* Schmid, 1876, probably a sediment-feeding trace of a polychaete. Middle Triassic (Anisian) limestone (Muschelkalk Group), Weimar, Germany. Right: *Chondrites bollensis* (Zieten) Schimper, 1869, maybe formed by a chemosymbiotic worm-like organism. Lower Jurassic (Toarcian) black shale of Holzmaden, Germany.

References

Buatois, L A and M Mángano (2011). *Ichnology: Organism–Substrate Interactions in Space and Time*. Cambridge University Press, Cambridge, 366 p.

Knaust, D (2012). Trace-fossil systematics. In: Knaust, D and Bromley, R G (eds), Trace Fossils as Indicators of Sedimentary Environments. *Developments in Sedimentology* **64**, 79–101.

Knaust, D (2014). Classification of bioturbation-related reservoir quality in the Khuff Formation (Middle East): towards a genetic approach. In: Pöppelreiter, M C (ed.), *Permo-Triassic Sequence of the Arabian Plate*. EAGE, 247–267.

Knaust, D and R Bromley (2012). Trace Fossils as Indicators of Sedimentary Environments. *Developments in Sedimentology* **64**. Elsevier, Oxford, 960 p.

Seilacher, A (2007). *Trace Fossil Analysis*. Springer, Berlin, 226 p.

A walk through time, part 1
Felix Gradstein

The international Geologic Time Scale (Gradstein et al. 2012; Figure 1 page 20) integrates available stratigraphic and geochronology information. It provides the relational framework for the physical, chemical, and biological processes on Earth. The time scale is crucial for understanding the dynamics of the five major biosphere collapses and extinctions through deep time. Humans have now induced a new and major biosphere upheaval.

Calibration to absolute (linear) time of the succession of events recorded in the rocks on Earth has three components:

1. The standard stratigraphic divisions and their correlation in the global rock record.

2. The means of measuring linear time or elapsed durations from the rock record.

3. The methods of effectively joining the two scales, the stratigraphic one and the linear one.

For historic reasons and convenience in communication, the rock record of Earth's history is subdivided in a chronostratigraphic scale of standardized global stratigraphic units, such as 'Ordovician', 'Miocene', 'Harpoceras falciferum ammonite Zone', or 'polarity Chron C24r'. Unlike the continuous ticking clock of the chronometric scale (measured in years before 'Present', which is defined as 2000 CE), the chronostratigraphic scale is based on relative time units, in which global reference points at boundary stratotypes define the limits of the main formalized units, such as 'Ediacaran' or 'Devonian.' The chronostratigraphic scale is an international-ratified convention based on the actual rock record, whereas its calibration to linear time is a matter for discovery or estimation. The suite of stage boundaries and definitions are compiled here: *engineering.purdue.edu/Stratigraphy*.

The radiometric (U-Pb and ^{40}Ar/^{39}Ar) and orbital-tuning methods that provide our geological clocks are becoming better calibrated. However, few (eight!) dates are directly on stage boundaries, hence interpolation methods are used to assign the ages to the majority of stage boundaries.

The history of life as calibrated by Geologic Time Scale 2012

In 1982, Raup and Sepkoski published a much-quoted study that identified five major biological mass extinctions. Further taxonomic data mining and improved analysis of the considerable data set (Sepkoski 2002), show the major extinctions and radiations (Figure 2, page 21). Among extinctions, the end of Ordovician, end of Permian, and end of Cretaceous show the strongest signal, although details and causes of these mass extinctions are complex and only partly understood. Among originations, the great Cambrian diversification, the Great Ordovician Biodiversification Event, and the post Cretaceous–Palaeogene boundary event recovery standout.

The major extinction events have been recognized for a very long time; in fact, they were the main reason for dividing the Phanerozoic into the Palaeozoic, Mesozoic, and Cenozoic eras. Having accurate ages for the GTS is a fundamental requirement for understanding the timing and rate of extinction, and the causal links between biotic and extra-biotic factors.

Life in the Precambrian

The Precambrian is at the dawn of a geologically meaningful stratigraphic scale. The oldest record of early life forms on Earth was recovered from the circa 3.49 Ga old Dresser Formation in the Pilbara Craton of Australia. Here, stromatolites and possible microfossils are preserved in a thin succession of carbonates, sandstones, and hydrothermal precipitates deposited under intermittently shallow-water conditions within a volcanic caldera setting. Later, circa 2.6 Ga, a significant increase in oxygenic relative to anaerobic photosynthesis is thought to have arisen, linked to a marked increase in ocean primary productivity.

The stratigraphy of the Cryogenian and Ediacaran periods of the latest Precambrian is developing rapidly, with many new chemostratigraphic, biostratigraphic, and radiometric correlation levels. The Ediacaran Period (635–541 Ma) marks a pivotal position in the history of life, between the microscopic, mostly prokaryotic assemblages that had dominated the classic 'Precambrian', and the large, complex, and commonly shelly animals that dominated the Cambrian and younger Phanerozoic periods. Diverse large spiny acritarchs and simple animal embryos occur immediately above the base of the Ediacaran and range through at least the lower half of the Ediacaran. The mid-Ediacaran Gaskiers glaciation (584–582 Ma) was immediately followed by the appearance of the Avalon assemblage of the largely soft-bodied Ediacara biota (579 Ma). The earliest abundant bilateral burrows and impressions (555 Ma) and calcified animals (550 Ma) appear towards the end of the Ediacaran Period.

A walk through time

Figure 1. The Geologic Time Scale 2012.

PHANEROZOIC

CENOZOIC

Age Ma	Period	Epoch	Age/Stage	Age Ma
0	Qual.	Holocene		
		Pleisto-cene	Calabrian	0.78
			Gelasian	1.81
	Neogene	Plio-cene	Piacenzian	2.59
			Zanclean	3.60
5				5.33
		Miocene	Messinian	7.25
10			Tortonian	11.63
			Serravallian	13.82
15			Langhian	15.97
			Burdigalian	20.4
20			Aquitanian	23.0
25	Paleogene	Oligocene	Chattian	28.1
			Rupelian	33.9
35		Eocene	Priabonian	37.8
40			Bartonian	41.2
45			Lutetian	47.8
50			Ypresian	56.0
55		Paleocene	Thanetian	59.2
60			Selandian	61.6
65			Danian	66.0

MESOZOIC

Age Ma	Period	Epoch	Age/Stage	Age Ma
70	Cretaceous	Late	Maastrichtian	72.1
80			Campanian	83.6
			Santonian	86.3
90			Coniacian	89.8
			Turonian	93.9
100			Cenomanian	100.5
110			Albian	113.0
120		Early	Aptian	126.3
130			Barremian	130.8
			Hauterivian	133.9
			Valanginian	139.4
140			Berriasian	145.0
150	Jurassic	Late	Tithonian	152.1
			Kimmeridgian	157.3
160			Oxfordian	163.5
		Middle	Callovian	166.1
170			Bathonian	168.3
			Bajocian	170.3
			Aalenian	174.1
180		Early	Toarcian	182.7
190			Pliensbachian	190.8
200			Sinemurian	199.3
			Hettangian	201.3
210	Triassic	Late	Rhaetian	209.5
220			Norian	228.4
230			Carnian	237.0
240		Middle	Ladinian	241.5
			Anisian	247.1
250		Early	Olenekian	250.0
			Induan	252.2

PALAEOZOIC

Age Ma	Period	Epoch	Age/Stage	Age Ma
	Permian	Lopin-gian	Changhsingian	254.2
			Wuchiapingian	259.8
		Guada-lupian	Capitanian	265.1
275			Wordian	268.8
			Roadian	272.3
		Cis-uralian	Kungurian	279.3
			Artinskian	290.1
300			Sakmarian	295.5
			Asselian	298.9
	Carboniferous (Pennsylvanian)	L	Gzhelian	303.7
			Kasimovian	307.0
		M	Moscovian	315.2
		E	Bashkirian	323.2
325	Carboniferous (Mississippian)	L	Serpukhovian	330.9
		M	Visean	346.7
350		E	Tournaisian	358.9
	Devonian	Late	Famennian	372.2
375			Frasnian	382.7
		Middle	Givetian	387.7
			Eifelian	393.3
400		Early	Emsian	407.6
			Pragian	410.8
			Lochkovian	419.2
425	Silurian	Pridoli		423.0
		Ludlow	Ludfordian	425.6
			Gorstian	427.4
		Wenlock	Homerian	430.5
			Sheinwoodian	433.4
		Llando-very	Telychian	438.5
			Aeronian	440.8
			Rhuddanian	443.4
450	Ordovician	Late	Katian	453.0
			Sandbian	458.4
		Middle	Darriwilian	467.3
			Dapingian	470.0
475		Early	Floian	477.7
			Tremadocian	485.4
	Cambrian	Furon-gian	Age 10	489.5
			Jiangshanian	494.0
			Paibian	497.0
500		Epoch 3	Guzhangian	500.5
			Drumian	504.5
			Age 5	509.0
		Epoch 2	Age 4	514.0
			Age 3	521.0
525		Terre-neuvian	Age 2	529.0
			Fortunian	541.0

PRECAMBRIAN

Age Ma	Eon	Era	Period	Age Ma
600	Proterozoic	Neoproterozoic	Ediacaran	635
700			Cryogenian	850
800				
900			Tonian	1000
1000				
1100		Mesoproterozoic	Stenian	1200
1200			Ectasian	1400
1300				
1400			Calymmian	1600
1500				
1600			Statherian	1800
1700		Paleoproterozoic		
1800			Orosirian	2050
1900				
2000				
2100			Rhyacian	2300
2200				
2300			Siderian	2500
2400				
2500	Archean	Neo-archean		2800
2600				
2700				
2800				
2900				
3000		Meso-archean		3200
3100				
3200				
3300				
3400		Paleo-archean		3600
3500				
3600				
3700		Eoarchean		
3800				
3900				4000
4000				
4100				
4200		Hadean (informal)		
4300				
4400				
4500				

Figure 2. Summary trend of animal diversity and extinctions through time.

Diversity

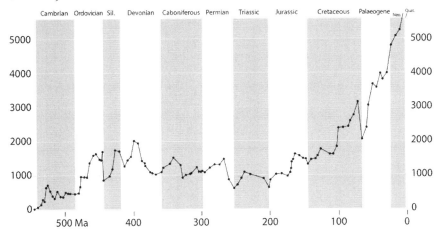

Extinction

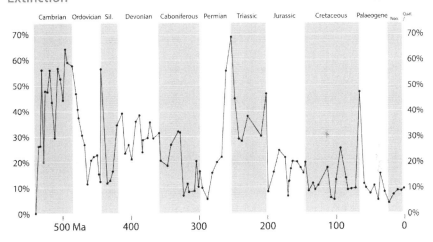

References and acknowledgments

Gradstein, F M, J Ogg, M Schmitz, G Ogg et al. (2012). *The Geologic Time Scale 2012*. Elsevier, Boston. 1144 p.

McNeely, J (2001). Invasive species: a costly catastrophe for native biodiversity. *Land Use and Water Resources Research*, **1** (2), 1–10.

Millennium Ecosystem Assessment (2005). *Ecosystems and Human Well-being: synthesis*. Island Press, Washington. 137 p.

D M Raup and J Sepkoski (1982). Mass extinctions in the marine fossil record. *Science* **215** (4539), 1501–1503.

Sepkoski, J (2002). A Compendium of Fossil Marine Animal Genera, ed. D Jablonski, M Foote. *Bulletin of the American Palaeontological Society* **363**, 1–560.

Øyvind Hammer kindly assisted with the update of Figure 2.

A walk through time, part 2
Felix Gradstein

Palaeozoic

The Cambrian Period (541–485 Ma) saw the advent of seafloor bioturbation by bottom feeders, the first major radiation of hard-shelled life (trilobites), and the appearance of vision in this group.

During the Ordovician Period (485–419 Ma), one of the greatest evolutionary radiations took place, generally referred to as the Great Ordovician Biodiversification Event. Starting in the middle Cambrian, marine biodiversity increased to reach a level (about 1600 genera) that was not significantly exceeded during the remainder of the Palaeozoic, or the early Mesozoic, or possibly up to the Palaeocene. Brachiopods, trilobites, corals, echinoderms, bryozoans, gastropods, bivalves, nautiloids, graptolites, and conodonts show major genus-level increases through the Ordovician. Then, near the end of the Ordovician, over 25 percent of all marine animal families, over 50 percent of genera, and over 80 percent of species became extinct, marking one of the largest faunal turnovers on Earth. Dramatic changes in niches due to platform and shelf reorganization, major climate change, and oceanographic perturbations may have been contributing factors.

During the Devonian (419–399 Ma), animals and early seed plants appeared on land. The animals include insects, amphibians (tetrapods), and lung fishes. The Devonian is also the time of greatest carbonate production with a peak of reef growth, and of the greatest diversity of marine fauna in the Palaeozoic. This ended in the late Devonian when major hypoxic or anoxic phases led to substantial mass extinctions. Over a period of perhaps 20 million years, a large number of families, genera, and species disappeared in the Frasnian and Famennian stages, including many trilobites.

In the Carboniferous (359–299 Ma), reptiles evolved and major glaciations reigned in southern Gondwana, the enormous assembly of Antarctica, Australia, India, and other parts of southern Asia, and parts of Africa and South America.

The end of Permian faunal and floral turnover about 252 Ma is the largest biological turnover event in history with the demise of over 55 percent of all faunal families, 80 percent of all genera, and over 95 percent of all species. The very last taxa of the prominent Palaeozoic trilobite group disappeared at the end of Permian. There is considerable evidence for a runaway greenhouse effect and significant increase in temperatures in the latest Permian and Early Triassic, possibly associated with the Siberian Trap volcanism. Associated charcoal-rich and soot-bearing layers indicate widespread wildfires on land.

Mesozoic

The so-called K–T extinction event, properly called the Cretaceous–Palaeogene extinction event, was followed by a radiation of mammals and birds during the Palaeocene. The event itself saw over 17 percent of all families, 50 percent of all genera, and over 75 percent of all species disappear on land, and sessile life in the ocean decreased over 30 percent. Among oceanic plankton, the foraminifera became nearly all extinct before rebounding with many new taxa in the Palaeocene. Dinosaurs were already on the way out before their final demise. The period boundary event is linked to the Chicxulub (Yucatan Peninsula) meteorite impact crater, 180 km across, in addition to the Deccan Trap volcanism.

Anthropocene

The late Holocene, the beginning of the Industrial Revolution, or the middle of the 20th century with its massive urbanization and nuclear explosions, are candidates for a new chronostratigraphic unit that has been termed Anthropocene.

Anthropogenic change to Earth's biota, both in the plant and in the animal kingdoms is now pervasive. Such changes are clearly visible both on land and in the sea. Extinction rates, the most obvious indicator of change, are currently perhaps 100–1000 times background rates (Millennium Ecosystem Assessment 2005). These very high rates are recent, and so Earth has thus far only lost a small proportion of its biodiversity (Figure 2). However, many more species are classed as threatened, endangered, or critically endangered, and the continuation of present trends could produce a mass extinction event comparable to the 'Big Five' of Phanerozoic history in as little as a few centuries.

Perhaps the most striking signal to date is that of cross-global species invasions, at a rate and on a scale unique in Earth's history. Terrestrial biotas worldwide now commonly include up to a quarter of total species (and up to a half of plant species) as invasive (McNeely 2001). Marine invasive species may be less in total, but are more rapidly growing. The numbers far exceed reported extinctions, with some 10 000 invasive species reported from Europe alone.

Thus ends our (too short) walk in deep time.

Adaptive landscape and genetic algorithms

Enrico Savazzi

The adaptive landscape is a theoretical construct, typically visualized as a surface in 3D-space resembling a mountainous landscape. Adaptiveness is plotted on the z-axis and reaches one or more maxima, called adaptive peaks. The x- and y-axes (and any additional dimensions) represent quantitative or qualitative biological variability.

Each individual occupies one point on the surface of the adaptive landscape, and each species occupies a typically contiguous area. Gene mutation and recombination randomly distribute new individuals at points generally not far from their parents, and selection rewards with a higher reproductive success the individuals located at higher z values.

Intraspecific variability typically bridges only narrow adaptive valleys. Unless broad valleys prevent further evolution toward a peak, a species evolves 'uphill' and eventually reaches the peak, where continued selection keeps it in place. A species has no 'knowledge' of regions of the adaptive landscape it does not occupy, so nearby adaptive peaks may very well remain unoccupied. McGhee (2007) provided an extensive discussion of adaptive landscapes, their history, and related concepts.

In computer programming, genetic algorithms (GAs) were inspired by evolution and are interesting in this context. These algorithms were not developed as accurate models of evolution, and a comparison with evolution should therefore be applied with caution.

In GAs, parameters correspond to genes. Program execution starts with a population of candidate solutions, each storing slightly different parameter values. Values in the next generation are computed by applying recombination and mutation to the parents' values. Finally, selection adjusts the probability of reproduction of each offspring, based on its optimality (z-value).

With empirical adjustments for specific problems, genetic algorithms are often successful in solving engineering problems — and with good solutions. However, no underpinning theory clearly explains why.

Like evolution, GAs cannot reach a global optimum (highest adaptive peak)

Genetic algorithms are often successful in solving
engineering problems — and with good solutions.
However, no underpinning theory clearly explains why.

separated from the population by a broad low-optimality region. In this case, GAs lead the population no further than a local optimum. The No Free Lunch theorem in optimization theory states that none of the alternative GA modifications to mitigate this problem can be more efficient than all others in all problems, i.e. there is no general solution.

The similarities of evolution with GAs suggest that evolution, in a rugged adaptive landscape, should be intrinsically poor in reaching far adaptive peaks, and cannot become much better. However, the ubiquitous occurrence of convergent evolution suggests that evolution is highly successful in reaching adaptive peaks (see *Constructional morphology and morphodynamics*). A proposed explanation involves generalist species, which occupy low-z regions and 'hop' among low adaptive peaks as stepping-stones to higher ones.

Another possible explanation for this disparity is that GAs fail to model evolution in critical respects: they make no distinction between genotype and phenotype, they cannot model gene interdependencies, and their solution space (the complete adaptive landscape) is static. Several evolutionary hypotheses rely instead on adaptive peaks that wander across the adaptive landscape. Some adaptive peaks may be continuously reshaped by evolution (e.g. once an ecological niche is occupied, it becomes less accessible to other species, or a numerically large population may deplete the resources on an adaptive peak and lower it, encouraging an exodus). Other peaks may be shaped by unalterable factors such as physical laws, and are sufficiently static to be reached multiple times. Wandering adaptive peaks may carry species across normally impassable valleys, and in this way allow species to reach even isolated static peaks.

It is not clear at present, and should be investigated, whether a mixed static–dynamic adaptive landscape versus a fully static or fully dynamic one results in significantly different evolutionary patterns and tempos.

References

McGhee G R Jr (2007). *The geometry of evolution.* University Press, Cambridge, 200 p.

Age is an interpretation

Mike Simmons

Every day geologists ask one another, 'What age is that outcrop/formation/log pick/seismic marker?' This deceptively simple question usually has a superficially simple answer, but an answer which masks a more complex thought process and which underlines the need for clarity of communication between stratigraphers and other geoscientists.

To communicate our answer to the 'What age is it?' question, we almost always turn to the formal language of chronostratigraphy with as much precision as we dare — 'It's Jurassic' or 'It's Bajocian' we will reply. Few listening to such an answer will realize that it is very much an interpretation and shorthand for what should really be a much longer statement — something such as, 'It contains an assemblage of dinoflagellate fossils indicative of the *Nannoceratopsis semex* biozone which in turn is currently calibrated with the *Strenoceras niortense* to *Parkinsonia parkinsoni* Tethyan ammonite biozones which currently form the standard biozones of the upper half of the Bajocian stage within the Jurassic system'. Am I being facetious? Not at all — this statement could have been much longer — for example, how sure am I that the fossil taxa present in the rocks really do indicate the *Nannoceratopsis semex* biozone?

When asked what is the value of biostratigraphy or palaeontology, students and experienced professionals alike invariably reply that fossils tell you the age of rocks, as though ammonites and trilobites can speak to us like sacred oracles. We should remind them that biostratigraphy is the science of subdividing strata on the basis of palaeontological characteristics, using biozones and associated defining events — typically extinctions or inceptions of taxa. Such locally defined biozones are then calibrated, through co-occurrences with age significant fossils and often through intermediate schemes of other fossil groups, to the standard zonation schemes (ammonites, graptolites, etc) that form the basis of defining the chronostratigraphic units every geologist is familiar with (Jurassic, Oxfordian, etc).

If that calibration process wasn't complex enough, using jumps between biostratigraphic schema based on co-occurrences and juxtapositions, there are often further levels of uncertainty. Although biostratigraphy has its roots in the early 19th century, the process of calibration from fossils in a rock to age

Age	Before 2004		After 2004	
Maastrichtian	A. mayaroensis ▲	Abathompalus mayaroensis	Pl. hantkeninoides	
			P. hariaensis	R. fructicosa ▼
				P. hariaensis ▲
	G. gansseri ▲	Gansserina gansseri	Abathompalus mayaroensis	A. mayaroensis ▲
			Racemiguembelina fructicosa	
	G. aegyptiaca ▲	Globotruncana aegyptiaca		R. fructicosa ▲
			Pseudoguembelina palpebra	P. palpebra ▲
		Globotruncanella havanensis		
	G. calcarata ▼		Gansserina gansseri	G. gansseri ▲
Campanian		Globotruncanita calcarata	Globotruncana aegyptiaca	G. aegyptiaca ▲
	G. calcarata ▲		Globotruncanella havanensis	
		Globotruncana ventricosa	Globotruncanita calcarata	G. calcarata ▼▲
	G. elevata ▲		Contusotruncana plummerae	C. plummerae ▲
		Globotruncanita elevata	Globotruncanita elevata	

interpretation is still ongoing. For example, fossils and related biozones once regarded as Maastrichtian are now regarded as indicative of older Campanian ages (the zones and events remain useful for correlation — only the age labels have changed; see figure above). None of this is helped by the fact that a number of the fundamental units of chronostratigraphy — stages — which in turn are the building blocks of systems, eras, and so on, lack formal definition. At the time of writing there is no definition of what fossil event or zone constitutes the Jurassic–Cretaceous boundary. Hence one stratigrapher may calibrate an assemblage of fossils to the lowermost Cretaceous while another may use a different definition of the system boundary and calibrate the same assemblage into the uppermost Jurassic.

This can cause endless confusion for the poor end-user geologist — the oracles are giving conflicting messages or changing their mind! I have lost count of the times that I have explained that despite finding the same fossils, two stratigraphers may put different age interpretations on these occurrences for good reasons. A formation at location X is reported as being Barremian while the same formation at location Y is reported as being Aptian. Is it a diachronous formation? Not necessarily — the different ages may simply be an artefact of changing calibration.

Let us return to that deceptively simple question, 'What age is it?'. Rarely is a numerical age sought. Usually the question is really an oblique way of asking, 'Does this rock correlate with this other rock?'. In many ways this is a much easier question to answer as subdivision and thence correlation of rocks on the basis of their fossil content at a local, regional, or global scale is often a more straightforward notion than the age label that usually accompanies this.

So my simple plea is to remind our fellow geologists that age is an interpretation and it is the fossil assemblage in the rock that matters. It is the zones defined by these assemblages that provide correlation, not the age labels we place upon them.

As good as it gets

Robert W Williams

It was one of the most rewarding projects of my career as a biostratigrapher. It was August 2011 and I analysed a microplankton slide for the first time while four geologists crowded behind me, peeking over my shoulder, fidgeting nervously, waiting for my assessment of the fossil assemblage. They asked, 'How old is it? Have you found anything? Is it older than Palaeocene?' One could sense the anxiety in their voice, as if they were afraid the microfossils would not agree with their expectations.

The sample under my microscope was very important. However, the palaeontologist must be street-smart when communicating with petroleum geologists. The latter are generally not interested in the nuts and bolts of palaeontology. Understandably, they want conclusions, not morphological details. They want to know ages and depositional environments, not Latin and Greek names. They want chronostratigraphic certainty, not the intricacies of taxonomy.

I had become accustomed long ago to lighthearted teasing about dinoflagellates from non-biostratigrapher co-workers. The tongue-in-cheek remarks were often hilarious, and contributed to a healthy, congenial working environment. Nevertheless, I had never thought I would see the day that my colleagues would grovel before my feet, begging to share in the knowledge that marine microplankton provide. I found their sudden respect for my science intensely rewarding. I savoured the moment.

The organic residue sealed in transparent polymer on the slide in my microscope had been submersed in hydrofluoric acid only a few minutes earlier. We dissolve the carbonates from sedimentary rock, then dissolve the silicates. What remains is the acid-resistant organic content of the sediment: microplankton, terrestrial spores, pollen, and the ever-present organic background debris. The acid digestion technique underpins the science of palynology.

The organic residue I was analysing originated from a claystone sample that we had retrieved the previous week from a seabed outcrop near the base of the Jan Mayen Ridge. Four hundred kilometres northeast of Iceland, sedimentary rocks outcrop along the steep cliffs of the ridge in 2000 m water depth. We had high-resolution seismic data across the ridge, but we had no information on the age of the seismic reflectors. If we knew the ages of the outcropping beds, we could assess the petroleum potential of the unexplored region south of the Jan Mayen micro-continent. In the summer of 2011, we successfully completed the first geological sampling mission in the area using a remotely operated vehicle, or ROV.

An exploration company had used a gravity corer to sample the outcrops years earlier. However, gravity core tubes are notorious for deflecting off steep inclines. In addition, because the core tool occasionally drops to the sea floor along a helical or meandering trajectory, the geographic coordinates of the sample point can have a large error ellipse on a slope. The ROV with high-resolution cameras and acoustic positioning transponders proved very successful in this respect.

After a few minutes of microscopy, and a few 'ohs' and 'hmms' as I peered into the oculars, I finally answered 'yes' to the geologists' question, 'Do you know the age?' 'Well then tell us!' they insisted. 'But if I tell you, then I will no longer be the only person on the planet who knows the age of these strata! I quite like being the only person who knows.'

I realized that I was experiencing the peak of my career in palaeontology. After all the years of friendly jabs, I was getting my revenge!

To my co-workers' great jubilation, I proclaimed that the sample's age was Early Cretaceous, around the Valanginian–Hauterivian boundary. They were elated because it proved that there are Mesozoic sediments on the Jan Mayen Ridge. Unfortunately, their joy was short lived. A few days later, high-resolution video from the ROV showed that samples having ages older than Eocene were not from the outcrop but were lying loose on the sea floor. They were part of the enormous debris field of dropstones from icebergs sourced from Greenland. Samples that the ROV's mechanical arm broke off the outcrop consistently contained Eocene and Early Oligocene dinoflagellate assemblages. It was an important discovery.

The path to robust biostratigraphical interpretations is often long and winding, but the fun is in the adventure of discovery of the earth's deep history. I feel very fortunate to be working with these lovely fossils. Dinoflagellate evolution produced innumerable fantastic morphologies, and it is always a pleasure to share them with those who appreciate them!

Bioastronomy

Simon Conway Morris

'Astrobiology is the study of things that do not exist'. A definition hardly less helpful than that for history: 'The study of things that did not happen by people who were not there'. Well, history thrives, and in its own quiet way so does astrobiology. Indeed there is a feeling of growing optimism. Even if there is still no smoking gun, early Mars is looking as promising as it ever did as a former abode of life. Slightly further afield Europa remains a candidate. And out in the wide black yonder? Thanks to *Kepler*, we know that it is teeming with extra-solar planets, so many that Earth-like worlds must be two a penny. Copernican mediocrity with a vengeance.

But all is written on promissory notes. Mars is being visited so often that it qualifies for Air Miles. As and when rock samples are returned to complement the 70-odd Martian meteorites, then maybe fossil cells or biomarkers lurking in Noachian sediments will show how life first stirred some 200 million miles from Earth (unless of course our planet was seeded by Martian colonists as the time of major bombardment drew to an end).

Such local panspermia would come as little surprise, but across the galaxy we assume each solar system is held in quarantine. What one day might we find? Here an interesting tension arises. Even if one doesn't subscribe to something like Fred Hoyle's intelligent interstellar Black Cloud, maybe some of us are suffering from a failure of imagination. What about silicon-based life forms or strange creatures disporting themselves in oceans of liquid hydrocarbons, where –100°C counts as a warm day? One needs to keep an open mind, but so too remind ourselves that silicon compounds have a habit of blowing up and at temperatures far below freezing metabolic rates would be, well, glacially slow.

Everybody reading this article is a carbaquist life form (or so I hope). There are strong arguments that all life depends on the versatility of carbon and the peculiar properties of water. Many would cautiously extend this universality to biochemistry. If extraterrestrials use DNA or employ chlorophyll for photo-synthesis, this should not come as any great surprise. So too the great major-ity of inhabited planets are probably pretty robust places, occupied only by extremophiles resistant to extremes of temperature, salinity, pressure, and so on. Such microbes are naturally a focus for astrobiologists. Less appreciated is

Even if the oceans are deeper or the atmosphere denser we can still predict the life forms. It's not rocket science, just biology.

that terrestrial extremophiles have explored nearly all of the available physico-chemical parameter space. No need to go 'abroad' — it's all been done here.

But what about complex biospheres? Here imagination runs wild, populating planets with a weird bestiary of aliens, principally repulsive. Steady on. First, basic physical parameters, such as Reynolds number and diffusion rates, impose rigid constraints on what is possible. Second, evolutionary convergence shows that the number of available solutions is restricted. Will aliens have eyes? Yes! And camera eyes? Again yes, if they are intelligent and about our size. If camera eyes (and olfaction and echolocation and …) are inevitable products of evolution, then so too will be nervous systems and intelligence. Remember that a good deal of the molecular machinery needed to make a nerve cell evolved long before the first animal. So too large brains, intelligence, and tool-making have evolved multiple times. So 'out there' will be eerily similar to 'down here'. Even if the oceans are deeper or the atmosphere denser we can still predict the life forms. It's not rocket science, just biology.

But there is one small snag. Our solar system is rather young, long predated by millions of others. With a head-start of four billion years (or more), one or other extraterrestrial civilization would have fanned across the galaxy. Earth would have been colonized and we simply wouldn't be here to study astrobiology. Let me reveal a secret. Enrico Fermi was right and his paradox holds. There is nobody out there and we are completely alone. As I said: astrobiology is the study of things that do not exist.

31

Biostratigraphy at a distance
Iain Prince

It is 2020 and drilling is reaching a critical point on the latest deepwater well in the Gulf of Mexico. Despite millions of dollars spent on acquiring new seismic data, the old problems of sub-salt imaging and drilling remain: we can't see what we think we are drilling. The solution is to call up a last millennium solution — biostratigraphy. Except on this well, despite the operations geologist asking, 'What does the biostratigraphy say?', there is no biostratigrapher on the rig, only a technician. That's because Shell is using its imaging microscope on this rig.

It was in 2011 when looking at the microscope in my office while waiting for a remote support person to fix my computer, that the idea hit me. Why couldn't we send a more modern microscope, with all its functionality controlled by a computer, to the wellsite and control the microscope remotely from onshore? The sedimentary petrologists in Shell have microscopes with image capture technology; by merging the two, we could build a potentially powerful new system.

The initial test of the concept was carried out in 2011, using a computer-aided petrology system located in Bernard Instruments office outside Houston, while I remained in Shell's office across town. Despite some latency issues, it was possible to connect and control the microscope remotely.

To overcome the lag time, it was decided that initially a low-resolution scan of the whole slide would be made. For palynology, this could be at ×400 which is sufficient to identify most larger dinoflagellates. For nannofossils, it would be at ×630 or ×1000. This image would be displayed to the remote user, who could then click on a fossil and have the microscope automatically move the stage back to view it live.

Imaging software was evolving fast through 2012 making it possible to scan complete slides quickly at multiple focus levels. This of course generates a huge number of big files, but compression techniques are also improving significantly, such that this is not the problem it once was. The image capture software scans the microscope field of view at multiple focus levels (typically seven), compresses these files, and sends them onshore where they are stitched back together. If important fossils cannot be identified because the image stack resolution is too poor, it is possible to either use the remote connection to get a live view of the

...The idea hit me. Why couldn't we send a more modern microscope, with all its functionality controlled by a computer, to the wellsite and control the microscope remotely from onshore?

fossil, or to get the microscope to re-scan the fossil at an increased resolution.

Subsequently, Gunilla Gard and Jason Crux at BHP Billiton successfully tested the system operationally twice at a wellsite. While the existing microscope works, from a size and durability point of view it is not satisfactory. It is a Zeiss AxioMager 2ZM which requires three large sturdy plastic cases to transport offshore. It also requires careful handling and setup. Bernard Instruments are building a much smaller specialized scope which includes all the required features but will fit into one sturdy plastic case. This will be finished by mid 2015.

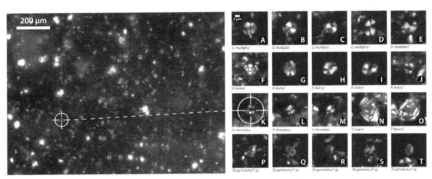

Theoretical example of fossils cut out from a scan and then streamed back in the form of a virtual database.

The next step is a nannofossil image recognition system, and this is also currently under development. Nannofossils are eminently suitable for this as, unlike dinoflagellates, they usually sit on the slide in a consistent orientation.

Image recognition for fossils has been tried numerous times over the last 25 years, usually with limited success. In some cases the shortfall has been attributable to a lack of computer processing power, or just that it has been applied to fossil groups that are inherently difficult to identify. But a number of technologies have improved to the point where a robust and fully operational system may be just around the corner.

Can you use pollen to catch criminals?

Julia Webb

Pollen is handy stuff. Apart from the plant fertilization process it is intended for, it has a wide variety of other uses: Fossilized pollen has been found in rocks dating back to the Carboniferous period proving the existence of primitive plants; bogs and lake sediments store fossilized pollen that can show vegetational succession from the last ice ages through to the present day; honey manufacturers use pollen trapped in their produce to test the provenance of suspect batches; doctors use it for allergy testing; and of course there's modern day crime-fighting.

Imagine you are a thief. You've just stolen something precious and jumped into your car and made your getaway. After some time you dump the car and run across a field and lose the police that are following you. You get home, and to cover your back you call the police and report your car stolen. Now, modern-day police have an arsenal of techniques to use at their disposal to help trace the last movements of people or objects, but in this case they have a hunch that you are lying and they seize your shoes. The soil on the sole of your shoes is all they need to be able to extract pollen and match it to the pollen in the soil of the field that they lost you in. Clever, huh?

Since the 1950s the study of pollen — called palynology — has been used to solve forensic cases in criminal courts. The assemblage of pollen found at a particular location can be so specific that it can be enough to convict on that basis alone. It doesn't need to be preserved in soil to be useful either. The outer shell of a pollen grain is very robust. And it gets everywhere: in dust, trapped in the weave of fabric, in your hair, under your nails, and even in your excrement!

It seems such a simple process, but there are some caveats to consider. Not all flowers produce the same amount of pollen. Different flowers shed different quantities of pollen depending on their dispersal method. A murder scene in woodland will offer a similar pollen assemblage across a large area, but finding single pollen grains of an insect pollinated bluebell (for example) can be significant. A murder case in Leeds, England, was partially solved by the pollen trapped in the victim's hair revealing a completely different location to the woodland that the body was discovered in. The mixture of garden weeds and cultivars led police to the perpetrator who was found guilty and sentenced to two life sentences.

The assemblage of pollen found at a particular location can be so specific that it can be enough to convict on that basis alone.

The preservation of pollen can also be a hindrance, although in most cases good preservation is an advantage! Often a case can involve 'unravelling' several different years of pollen stratigraphy, and if a depth of soil is involved then it can be several millennia. In a case in New Zealand, a tenant farmer was incorrectly convicted of drugs offences when cannabis pollen was found in the farm outbuildings. It later transpired that the pollen was residual from the previous occupier of the farm and the tenant was acquitted.

Pollen can also travel long distances. It's a handy feature for those plants relying on wind as their dispersal mechanism, but it can be confusing for palynologists when a particular species turns up hundreds or even thousands of kilometres from the nearest plants. *Ambrosia* pollen from plants growing on the east coast of the United States is often found in western Scotland.

Then there's plant maturity: it takes 15 years, sometimes more, for certain tree species to reach sexual maturity. For those years they are not producing pollen. In one case of a missing body, police seized the garden tools of a suspect. The pollen from the soil on the spades sent police looking for the victim's grave in mature pine and birch forests. The body was later discovered by dog walkers in a plantation of immature hemlock. The trees were not mature enough to produce pollen so they left no trace.

Crime shows on TV don't really do this branch of forensic science justice. Machines and flashy tools aren't used in palynology. Old fashioned microscopy and a skilled palynologist are all it might take to catch a crook.

Acknowledgments

This essay was inspired by a blog post by the author from March 2014; *uglosbioscience.wordpress.com*. References for the cases cited in the essay can be obtained by contacting the author at *jwebb@glos.ac.uk*.

Celebrate the power of plants

Imogen Poole

Its unique orbit within the 'Goldilocks zone' renders planet Earth habitable. For over 450 million years the unique ability of plants, from microscopic algae to mighty *Sequoias*, to harvest sunlight and change carbon dioxide and water into sugar while releasing oxygen has created a habitable world for millions of animal species, including ourselves. Without the 'Cinderella of science' — the boring botany bit (Willis 2014) — life as we know it would not have been possible.

Ever since they first appeared, plants have littered the earth with evidence of their presence (one of the few attributes they share with humans). Then, through geological processes, fragments of this litter have been preserved in the rock record. Reading the palaeobotanical evidence begins with rigorous yet painstaking observation, identification, interpretation, and classification. A necessary step since all subsequent research depends on these fundamental conclusions, but challenging given its subjective nature. Plants, being organic entities, do not always fit neatly into classification schemes, thus complicating and challenging our preconceptions. But embrace this challenge and 'boring botany' can provide insights into probable continental connections, vegetation zonations, climate, and the evolution of biochemical pathways. Perhaps not so boring after all!

Let's take a simple example. Trees have evolved over millions of years adapting to their environment, modifying their physical shape and internal functioning to maximize success and cope with competition. We can make observations on several scales:

- Macro-characters disclose form, habit, stature, and support;
- Meso-characters reveal shapes and sizes of flowers and leaves, as well as visible protective strategies;
- Micro-characters testify to reproductive strategies, stomatal responses, and chemical makeup.

Now look at the fossil record. Local vegetation can be derived directly from identifying wood, whose role is support not dispersal. Contrast this with leaves and their greater ability to disperse into the wider depositional setting. Pollen (or spores in the cryptogams) and seeds evolved for dispersal over long distances and therefore evidence a regional flora. When we compare these assemblages across continents, we start to understand past ecosystems and biomes.

The interaction between plant and environment is inherently interlinked. Fossilized plant parts act as proxies for environmental factors (Poole & van Bergen 2006):

- Growth rings record the relative favourability of the habitat, length of growing season, forest productivity, and insect infestation.
- Leaf cuticle thickness relates to aridity.
- Leaf size shows climate type.
- Stomata indicate relative deep-time pCO_2.
- Carbon and oxygen atoms in ligno-cellulose compounds record past atmospheric changes.

So one fossilized tree can provide numerous signals pertaining to both the local and regional environment. Extrapolate this to all plant parts and taxa, and the potential is enormous.

Yet obstacles, like Cinderella's stepsisters, stand in the way. Trends in society drive funding initiatives, which determine the direction of scientific research. The ever-increasing demand to find a quick fix shouldn't impede rigorous data gathering and analysis. Data sets need to be as large as possible, allowing plant taxa (beginning at the species level) to be traced back through geological time. Base lines need to be anchored in modern plant science and systematics. Duly acknowledging inherent uncertainty and alternative interpretations, and accepting that past plants and environments may have no modern analog, ensures robust and rigorous extrapolations from like-with-like character comparisons. Let's embrace what we find, accept that the natural world is more inventive than we often suppose, and invest time and money building solid foundations for future developments.

The Cinderella of science is ready for her unveiling. Let's celebrate her contribution to our Goldilocks world by giving her the accolades she deserves.

References

Poole, I and P van Bergen (2006). Physiognomic and chemical characters in wood as palaeoclimate proxies. *Plant Ecology*. **182**, 175–195.

Willis, K (2014). Plants: From Roots to Riches: Radio 4 airs epic series on plants. *The Independent*. Available at *ageo. co/1svst1O*

Constructional morphology and morphodynamics

Enrico Savazzi

Constructional morphology is one of the seminal concepts of 20th century palaeobiology, and has inspired the publication of hundreds of scientific papers. In a low-key announcement of a research project at Tübingen University, Adolf Seilacher (1970) introduced constructional morphology as a practical framework for analysing the morphology of organisms. He proposed that this morphology results from the interplay of three aspects, or factors: phylogenetic tradition, construction, and function. That paper contains a diagram (often reproduced in subsequent literature) with the three aspects located at the vertices of a triangle. The triangle diagram is not meant to be used as a quantitative graph, but only as a visual metaphor of the triple-aspect approach. Knowledge of this framework was subsequently spread among American palaeontologists largely by David M Raup.

Phylogenetic tradition includes genes presumably shared by a taxon, albeit not necessarily expressed in all its species. This aspect can help to explain parallel evolution within a group. Construction deals with growth, morphogenesis and self-assembly of an organism. Function is seen as an adaptive strategy, a synergic set of functional characters. The three aspects are often treated as constraints that limit the evolutionary choices available to a taxon.

Other definitions of constructional morphology exist, for example a group of largely German palaeontologists subscribes to a somewhat different concept. The term is also used, in unrelated ways, in linguistics and geology. This discussion deals only with Seilacher's definition.

Constructional morphology has been applied to fossil and extant species, albeit in the latter case largely by palaeontologists. Thus, these studies tend to concentrate on skeletal parts likely to be preserved in fossils, although the conceptual framework has no such limitation.

A common feature of papers in constructional morphology is attention to extreme adaptations and life histories, on the assumption (often justified by the results) that unusual sets of adaptations may be easier to interpret in evolutionary and functional terms. This attention to unusual case histories is sometimes dismissed as 'storytelling' by its critics.

Attention to extreme adaptations and life histories…
is sometimes dismissed as 'storytelling' by its critics.

Other common patterns in constructional morphology studies are the analysis of convergent evolution, particularly easy to recognize in extreme adaptations, and the comparative analysis of multiple taxonomic groups. I think these applications prove that constructional morphology can transcend storytelling and provide conclusions of general significance. For instance, these studies provide strong evidence that the number of possible adaptive strategies, or peaks in the adaptive landscape, is finite and small (see *Adaptive landscape and genetic algorithms*). Furthermore, some elements of constructional morphology have been applied in bionics.

It has been occasionally proposed to add numerous other aspects to Seilacher's original framework. However, multiple aspects make the categorization of an organism's features more difficult and subjective, without appearing to provide significant advantages. But Seilacher subsequently introduced biological morphodynamics as an apparent successor to constructional morphology, adding a fourth aspect — the environment immediately surrounding the organism — to the conceptual framework and, predictably, a tetrahedral diagram with the four aspects as vertices. In a private conversation (between 1995 and 2000), Seilacher explained morphodynamics as largely a way to avoid conflict with scientists keen to argue that their interpretation of constructional morphology was more correct. Nonetheless, I found morphodynamics fruitful, especially in sessile organisms permanently committed to their immediate environment.

References

Seilacher, A (1970). Arbeitskonzept zur Konstruktions-Morphologie. *Lethaia*, **3**, 393–396.
Seilacher, A and A Gishlick (2014). *Morphodynamics*. CRC Press. 551 p.

Decoding Quaternary sea levels

Martin Bates

Raised beaches and estuarine sediments tell us about past sea levels. They are key evidence in Quaternary science, the branch of geology that investigates the ice ages, and can often be associated with floral, faunal, and human remains. Geologists Charles Lyell (1838) and Joseph Prestwich (1859) were among the first to correctly recognize the remains of these ancient strandlines and their observations were built on in the 20th century by researchers such as Fredrick Zeuner (1959). Today we recognize such features in many locations including Australia, New Zealand, Papua New Guinea, and the west coast of the United States (Murray-Wallace & Woodroffe 2014).

In northwest Europe the evidence falls into two types of sequences:

- Former strandline and intertidal–subtidal deposits
- Estuarine sediments

Strandline deposits are well preserved on the Sussex and Hampshire coastal corridor where at least four chronologically discrete sequences are recognized (Bates et al. 2010). The best-known of these are the marine sediments preserved 40 m above sea level at Boxgrove in West Sussex. Here a beach and marine sand sequence is preserved and sealed by a regressive facies of sands and silts and an overlying land surface. The site also demonstrates the close relationship between Palaeolithic archaeology and Quaternary science because extensive evidence for

Marine sands overlain by cold climate solifluction deposits, Boxgrove, West Sussex.

human activity around 0.5 million years ago — in the form of flint knapping scatters, butchered animals, and even the remains of the humans themselves — lies on the preserved land surface (Roberts & Parfitt 1999). Similar, although probably younger, sequences occur on the south side of the English Channel at places such as Sangatte, France.

In contrast to the coarse sand and gravel sequences of former strandlines further inland we often see sediments belonging to the estuaries of rivers such as the Thames, Somme, or Seine, and river systems such as the Solent that no longer exist. Estuarine deposits can be extensive, for example those at Stone Point in Hampshire in the estuary of the former Solent River, or restricted, such as small tidal channels like those preserved around Selsey Bill. Significantly, these channels may contain a wide range of palaeoenvironmental indicators including large and small mammal remains, molluscs, foraminifera, ostracods, pollen, plant remains, and insects. These biological remains allow us to reconstruct the local environment and climate history and also let us apply biostratigraphy to the dating or correlation of such sites.

The importance of these sequences is in preserving a record of land and sea interaction during periods of high sea level and consequently they provide a yardstick for change in the Quaternary, comparable to river terrace records. The preservation of these sequences is, however, dependent on their topographic and tectonic setting. For example, preservation of sequences will only occur where emerging shorelines dominate as a result of tectonic or isostatic uplift. Here uplift elevates the sequences beyond the likely envelope of marine erosion during subsequent high sea-level events. Today the challenge for Quaternary scientists is to apply a robust chronological framework to these deposits in order for us to fully understand the interaction between climate change, sea-level history, and the way in which our species has adapted to such changes in the past.

References

Bates, M R, R Briant, E Rhodes, J Schwenninger, and J Whittaker (2010). A new chronological framework for Middle and Upper Pleistocene landscape evolution in the Sussex/Hampshire Coastal Corridor. *Proceedings of the Geologists' Association* 121, 369–392.

Lyell, C (1838). Address delivered at the anniversary meeting of the Geological Society of London, on the 17th February 1837. *American Journal of Science and Arts* 33, 76–117.

Murray-Wallace, C V and C Woodroffe (2014). *Quaternary Sea-Level Changes. A global perspective.* Cambridge University Press, Cambridge.

Prestwich, J (1859). On the westward extension of the old raised beach of Brighton and on the extent of the sea-bed of the same period. *Quarterly Journal of the Geological Society of London* 15, 215–221.

Roberts, M B and S Parfitt (1999). *Boxgrove: A Middle Pleistocene hominid site at Eartham Quarry, Boxgrove, West Sussex.* English Heritage Archaeological Report 17. English Heritage, London.

Zeuner, F E (1959). *The Pleistocene Period. Its Climate, Chronology and Faunal Successions.* Hutchinson Scientific and Technical, London. 447 p.

Dinosaur rock stars

Trine Krathus-Larsen

Just before Christmas last year my son, who was five years old at the time, came to me with a really cool drawing of a dinosaur. He told me that it was a *Triceratops* — and I would like to share it with you.

But the drawing made me think. When I was about the same age as my son I thought that dinosaurs were cool too, but at that time in the late 1970s and beginning of the 1980s dinosaurs didn't have the same status as they have today. Nobody really talked about them, you didn't find so many different kinds in the toy store and you did not see them on TV, so when I got older I kind of forgot about them. It was not until I went on an excursion with my class when I was about 18 years old that I re-discovered them. We went to Paris and Strasbourg, visiting several exhibitions with fossils and dinosaurs, and I remembered how amazing it all was. My class mates thought I was weird, but I didn't care.

Looking at my son's drawing, I started thinking about the resurgence that the dinosaurs have been going through the last 30 years or so. It took off at the beginning of the 1990s when the movie *Jurassic Park* was released. At the end of the 90s, the BBC aired an amazing series called *Walking with Dinosaurs*. I went to see the exhibition based on the TV show in Glasgow and I was really impressed. Children were able to race against a *Tyrannosaurus rex* — a highlight of the exhibition!

But this resurgence has not stopped yet. Kids learn about them from TV —

Every time my son asks me if we can read something about dinosaurs, we do it. Let's wait and see if this will result in a new biostratigrapher in about 20 years.

Dinosaur Train is a fantastic way for children to be informed and entertained at the same time. Sometimes I wish I was a kid in today's world.

Dinosaurs seem to have a special rock star status — at least among younger kids — and this is our opportunity to take it to the next level. Why not make a TV program called 'Swimming with dinoflagellates' or 'Floating with foraminifera'? Or in biology classes at school why not show living dinoflagellates, diatoms, or foraminifera? Catch a kid sneezing with hay fever and take an air sample to find out what type of plant, grass, or tree pollen is causing it. Pack your kids off to school with half your fossil collection, or give a presentation to their class on rocks and fossils. I think that if we could show more of this excitement to children, then some of them would be curious enough to learn more.

Society has a need for biostratigraphers for the foreseeable future and I believe that if we can keep children interested in dinosaurs and fossils, we might be able to take them a step further and make them more interested in the smaller life forms that were present, and in earth's history in general. In the current climate of cost cutting in industry, biostratigraphy is an efficient and cost-conscious tool for palaeoenvironmental analysis, subdividing stratigraphy, and correlating between wells. At the same time, with ever more focus on safe drilling, biostratigraphy has much to offer in terms of stratigraphic drilling control at the wellsite. The challenge for industrial biostratigraphers both now and in the future is communication. As well as pushing their science forward, they have to stand tall and shout loudly so as not to become invisible in what is a very competitive and demanding workplace.

We need to be creative to recruit more young people into the world of biostratigraphy and keep them motivated. So every time my son asks me if we can read something about dinosaurs, we do it. Let's wait and see if this will result in a new biostratigrapher in about 20 years.

Dinosaurs were not failures

Donald Henderson

There seems to be a sense among the general public that dinosaurs were failures. After all, they're all dead and long gone, and isn't that a sure sign of failure? The real fact is that extinction is the fate of all animal groups. Despite that inevitability, dinosaurs survived a major extinction at the end of the Triassic that eliminated a wide assortment of other large, fierce, and exotic reptiles. And, as is now widely accepted, dinosaurs are not truly gone — they persist in the form of birds today. However, in the remainder of this essay, the word 'dinosaur' will refer to the original, not-including-birds concept of dinosaurs.

One way of demonstrating that dinosaurs were not failures is that they were around for roughly 166 million years, first appearing as body fossils in the Middle Triassic about 232 million years ago. Compare that to something like the almost-as-famous, non-dinosaur *Dimetrodon* and its close relatives, which inhabited the planet for about 25 million years. There are tantalizing hints, in the form of distinctive three-toed fossil tracks, that dinosaurs may have been present in the earliest Triassic, not long after the most severe mass-extinction known — the end-Permian — implying that dinosaurs may have existed 250 million years ago. To give another sense for just how long dinosaurs existed, it is interesting to note that we are closer in time to *Tyrannosaurus* from the latest Cretaceous at 66 Ma than *Tyrannosaurus* was to *Allosaurus* from the Late Jurassic at 155 Ma. A time gap of 89 million years separates these two well-known theropods.

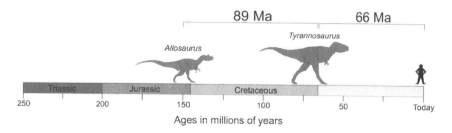

Ages in millions of years

Another indication of the success of dinosaurs is the huge range of body sizes that they evolved. They ranged in size from thrush- and chicken-sized forms weighing just a few tens of grams to the absolutely immense mid-Cretaceous,

Another common misconception is that dinosaurs had ridiculously small brains for their size, thus predisposing them to be failures and go extinct.

South American sauropods such as *Argentinosaurus* that are estimated to have weighed 80–100 tonnes. Excluding the aquatic whales which don't have to support their bodies against gravity, the largest land mammals known to have existed are creatures such as *Paraceratherium* from the Oligocene of Asia, with a body mass estimated to be 16 tonnes. While a very large animal, it weighed less than a quarter that of *Argentinosaurus.*

Another common misconception is that dinosaurs had ridiculously small brains for their size, thus predisposing them to be failures and go extinct. It has been well established by experimental studies over the past 70 years that brain size in all animals does not increase at the same rate as body size. In fact, reptiles have smaller brain volumes than mammals for a given body size, so dinosaurs were just following the reptile trend. Furthermore, large animals have proportionally smaller brains than do small animals: the ratio of brain to body mass in an elephant is less than that for a mouse.

No animal group can be considered to be perfect, and dinosaurs were no exception. Although attaining immense body sizes, existing for many tens of millions of years, and having their remains found on all the continents, there were some things that dinosaurs never did accomplish. Classical dinosaurs never evolved any aquatic forms. This may be due to the fact that Jurassic and Cretaceous seas were already home to other aquatic reptiles such as the plesiosaurs, ichthyosaurs, and turtles. Alternatively, it may be that the spines, hips, and legs of dinosaurs were so well adapted for supporting great body weights on land, that they could not be modified by natural selection to become effective for living in water. In contrast, aquatic mammals in the form of early whales began to appear within 20 million years of the extinction of the dinosaurs. Lastly, despite existing for at least 166 million years, dinosaurs never did evolve a tool-using culture. Mammals, in the form of early hominids, accomplished this within 64 million years of dinosaur extinction, a little more than a third of total dinosaur time.

In summary, we can see that dinosaurs were not failures, but just animals that were dealt a bad hand by the solar system in the form of an asteroid impact at the end of the Cretaceous.

Don't lose your plagiosaur

Tony Doré

Let me first declare my fraudulent credentials — I'm not a palaeontologist, I'm an oilman. But, like many geologists, my love of the science started in early adolescence, in my case when I first stumbled on the wonder of fossils while out hiking the Derbyshire Dales with my parents. Even now, after a long career dominated by seismic, logs, and petroleum systems, occasionally something happens to bring back that initial thrill. So I want to tell you about such a once-in-a-lifetime event that took place on a trip to Arctic Norway's Svalbard archipelago in 1984, ostensibly to study the petroleum potential of the Barents Sea.

The Arctic is one of the world's last great wildernesses. As a first-time visitor, I felt as if I was seeing everything with the first human eyes. I thought of Mary Anning walking the pristine Dorset shores a century or more before. Around the next corner, one might just stumble on something new and amazing. So it was that we were scrambling up the Upper Triassic shales of Miseryfjellet (Mount Misery) on Bear Island, the tiny frozen island south of Spitsbergen immortalized in Alistair MacLean's novel. Most of the party weren't interested in fossils and had ploughed on to the summit, while a couple of us were taking it more slowly, hoping for one of the rare Triassic ammonites that turned up from time to time.

Suddenly we spotted a few fossilized bones lying around, and excitedly started excavating — no doubt in a highly unprofessional way. Can you blame us? This was one of those cathartic moments I was telling you about. Hiding under large

siltstone slabs we found more bones, including a backbone, rib cage, and skull, enough to show that this was a sizeable vertebrate. Then, to our astonishment, on lifting another slab we found… a sardine can! My acute geological insight told me immediately that this wasn't a Triassic can, so what was the explanation? A Norwegian friend had the answer; he remembered hearing a story that one of Norway's largest fossil vertebrates had been found — then lost again — on Bear Island many years before.

It turns out that the fossil, a giant amphibian, had been discovered during a Cambridge University ecological survey in the year of my birth, 1948. The party lacked the equipment to collect and curate the hundreds of bone pieces, so they took a few samples for study then covered the amphibian up again. A letter to *Nature* by J Lowy in 1949 described the find, and remarked that it was unlikely that the fossil would survive the ravages of the next few winters. But after briefly breaking the surface for the first time in 210 million years, our amphibian wasn't to be denied. In all probability it was further covered by slippage of scree material, allowing it to be preserved until we stumbled on it 36 years later. A bit of later detective work in dusty museum corridors resulted in us finding the original expedition's bone material and photographs. The photos showed the same fossil, albeit in slightly better condition. And there, sitting among the ribs and presumably for scale, was a gleaming new sardine can!

The amphibian is a plagiosaur, probably related to the genera *Plagiosternum* or *Gerrothorax*, but much larger than any known species of either. At 3 m (nearly 10 ft) long, it is considerably larger than any living amphibian. These forms supposedly had salamander-like external gills and are characterized by broad, shield-like skulls — the Bear Island amphibian's skull is an impressive 70 cm wide. The fossil was airlifted by helicopter off the slopes of Miseryfjellet with a little help from oil company money, and taken to the Palaeontological Museum in Oslo for restoration.

A friend and I published a brief note on the rediscovery, but unfortunately, that's where the story currently ends. Apparently decisions at the museum fell under the sway of a trilobite man who held all fossils younger than Silurian in contempt, and the restoration never took place. So one of Norway's most unique fossils fell victim to palaeontological tribalism, and our giant amphibian waits patiently to emerge into the light for the third time.

References

Doré, A G and B Wandaas (1985). Lost fossil amphibian of Bear Island. *Geological Curator* **4** (3), 169–171.

Lowy, J (1949). A labyrinthodont from the Trias of Bear Island, Spitsbergen. *Nature* **163**, 1002.

Romer, A S (1971). *Vertebrate Palaeontology*. University of Chicago Press. 468 p.

Don't quote me on this

Øyvind Hammer

I will give you some straightforward facts and observations. Then I will draw a conclusion that is utterly unreasonable and probably untrue.

The hugely popular book *The World Without Us* (Weisman 2007) discusses what might happen to the earth if humans disappeared tomorrow. Weisman argues that after only a few centuries, few if any traces of us would be left. A similar book, *The Earth After Us* (Zalasiewicz 2009) speculates about traces of mankind in the future geological record. A hundred million years from now there would be little direct evidence that we were here. Our 100 000 years of existence as a species would be represented by perhaps a metre of stratigraphy. Through most of that time, we were exceedingly rare and did not fossilize well because of our terrestrial habitat. Cities and dams may last for a while, but eventually they will erode or be tectonically subducted.

As geologists we have been taught that 'the present is the key to the past'. Uniformitarianism, although not universally applicable, has been an invaluable tool for understanding geological processes in deep time. It could be suggested that we are now in a period of mass extinction caused by the actions of an intelligent species. We know of several mass extinctions in the geological past — by the principle of uniformitarianism, what should be our null hypothesis for the cause of these previous extinctions?

Zalasiewicz suggests that a negative carbon isotope excursion will be one of the few long-term traces of the human episode. Some previous mass extinctions, in particular the event at the end of the Permian, but also some minor events such as the end of the Palaeocene, are associated with precisely such negative carbon isotope excursions. Again, by the principle of uniformitarianism, what should be our null hypothesis for the cause of these excursions?

By now, it may have dawned on you what I'm getting at (of course, just for the record, being a serious man and fond of my job, I don't really mean it). I'm saying that it would not be surprising if civilizations in the geological past would have been hitherto unnoticed by geologists and palaeontologists. Instead of searching for alien civilizations in outer space, we might have better chances searching for them on Earth back in time, where we demonstrably had ecosystems to support them. Where should we look? In marine sediments perhaps, where remains of their magnificent sunken ships might have been preserved. In ancient hydrocarbon reservoirs perhaps, where their mighty drilling equipment could have fossilized. Or even better perhaps (as suggested to me by physicist Galen Gisler), on the moon and Mars, where their scientific landers might have remained unscathed through millions of years.

The idea that evolution is progressive is now out of fashion among biologists. Humans are no longer considered to be at the top of the heap. Evolution has not been a long march with the sole purpose of producing us as a finale. So why should we believe that nothing similar has happened before? To claim that we are the only intelligent species through time has the same philosophical status as claiming that we are the only intelligent species in the universe. It's unscientific.

Hang on, you say. Maybe we would not find their buildings or skeletons, but surely we should find their evolutionary precursors? Not so. Consider the fossil record of primates. It is almost non-existent, just some scraps here and there. Another 50 million years of erosion and subduction, and it will be virtually gone. Here is one possible scenario, out of many: there was a tree-living synapsid in the Permian, called *Suminia*. Here it is, below, together with the primate Ida (*Darwinius masillae*) from the Eocene. Which is which? Give Ida 50 million years, and she turns into us. Give *Suminia* 50 million years, and we are in the late Triassic. Could she have turned into something similar? Yes. Would we have fossil evidence for such an evolutionary sequence? Probably not.

Think about it. But don't quote me on this.

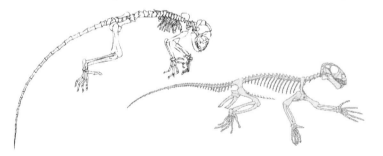

Left: *Darwinius* (redrawn by Jørn Hurum; after Franzen et al. 2009). Right: *Suminia* (after Fröbisch and Reisz 2009).

References

Franzen, J L, P Gingerich, J Habersetzer, J Hurum, W von Koenigswald, H Smith (2009). Complete primate skeleton from the Middle Miocene of Messel in Germany: Morphology and paleobiology. *PLoS ONE* **4** (5) e5723.

Fröbisch, J and R Reisz (2009). The Permian herbivore Suminia and the evolution of arboreality in terrestrial vertebrate ecosystems. *Proceedings of the Royal Society B*, **276**, 3611–3618.

Weisman, A (2007). *The World Without Us*. Thomas Dunne Books / St Martin's Press, 336 p.

Zalasiewicz, J (2009). *The Earth After Us*. Oxford University Press, 272 p.

Draw carefully

Jason A Dunlop

Modern palaeontology increasingly benefits from new and exciting methods. Techniques such as computed tomography have revolutionized our field, providing high-quality, often three-dimensional, images of the fossils in question. Yet I believe there is still a role for old-fashioned drawings; although these days a graphics tablet and associated software offer more comfortable ways of making illustrations than painstakingly inking an image onto tracing paper, shading it dot for tiny dot, and scraping away every minuscule mistake with a scalpel!

But why take the trouble to illustrate fossils at all? Isn't a decent photograph sufficient? It's an old, but true, adage that a picture paints a thousand words, but a good scientific illustration isn't just a pretty picture — it is also part of a hypothesis. Not all fossils are perfectly preserved, and from the mass (or sometimes mess) of lines, scratches, or imperfections in the rock matrix, palaeontologists have to tease out what is biologically relevant — what really belonged to the original organism — and what is unimportant or distracting. These distinctions are often crucial to how the fossil is being interpreted, and are not obvious in a raw photograph.

Taking time to draw a fossil carefully under the microscope helps me better understand the specimen by forcing me to make decisions about what I

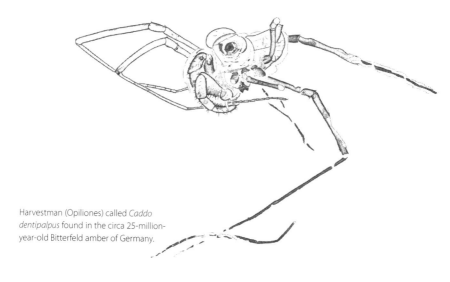

Harvestman (Opiliones) called *Caddo dentipalpus* found in the circa 25-million-year-old Bitterfeld amber of Germany.

A good drawing outlives its illustrator, and will go beyond the original function of describing how a new species looked.

can really see. Is this a leg I see before me? In the 19th century palaeontologists sometimes employed professional artists who may have spent more time looking at the material than did the scientists themselves. There are animals described as blind, even though the artist clearly put eyes on the accompanying illustration. In my own field of arthropod palaeontology it is important to accurately determine features like the number and boundaries of the body segments, the joints between the limbs or the mouthpart elements, and whether other details (eyes, spines, tubercles, and so on) are really present.

Done well, drawings offer valuable data for subsequent study, possibly years or even decades later. A good drawing outlives its illustrator, and will go beyond the original function of describing how a new species looked. High-quality figures can be used by later workers to recognize characteristics relevant for subjects such as functional morphology, or for determining evolutionary relationships. It is disappointing to receive a new publication about a potentially exciting fossil in which drawings are sketchy, or even absent, as this makes it harder to tell whether the authors have interpreted things correctly. If they claim an arthropod had 10 segments, but I suspect it should have had 11, then a drawing where they offer evidence for their count (and which can be compared directly to a photograph) would be extremely helpful.

Of course different researchers may interpret the same fossil in different ways, and this should be reflected in the relevant illustrations. For example, there is an early arthropod specimen *Fuxianhuia* in which some workers see extra limbs tucked under the body and others see the same structures as part of the internal digestive system. A drawing alone will not resolve this debate, but it touches on another decision the palaeontologist has to make. How much effort goes into the interpretative drawing? Should I draw the specimen to the best of my ability exactly as it appears in the rock? This is the more time-consuming alternative — which I personally favour — and assumes that all the anatomical features that are really there will emerge through the high-quality illustration. Others take a more schematic approach, and restrict the drawing to only those outline features which they consider relevant and necessary. This is quicker, and admittedly yields a neater picture, but risks overlooking finer details.

BASICS · METHODS · COMMUNICATION

Fossil hunting on eBay

Jørn H Hurum

I found a fossil on eBay some weeks ago. It was a 74-million-year-old ammonite from Montana, USA. Ammonites are an extinct group of shelled cephalopods, common as fossils in Mesozoic marine sediments. But this fossil looked different from hundreds of other ammonites offered on eBay. I arranged for the Friends of the Palaeontological Museum in Oslo, Norway, to buy the fossil and donate it to the museum.

The ammonite is named *Placenticeras meeki* and is rather large, about 35 cm across, flattened and boringly white, no nice mother of pearl preserved. Why did I bother to get this for the museum? It was because of small round holes in the shell. A scientific discussion of the origin of such holes in ammonite shells has raged since the 1960s. There are two main contestants: the boring gastropod theory and the more exciting bite theory.

Boring gastropods, in this instance limpets, are seen by some palaeontologists as the most likely perpetrators of the round holes. Limpets do not usually penetrate the shell they are grazing on, but they can thin it considerably. The thin spot could then break during compaction or preparation leaving nice round holes in the shell. In many instances the holes in ammonite shells looks rather haphazardly placed and could support the idea of limpets moving around on a shell.

The more exciting bite theory is based on the presence of one of the fiercest predators in the Cretaceous sea, the mosasaur. A mosasaur was a swimming relative of the Komodo dragon, only bigger. They grew to be up to 17.5 m long and had large pointy teeth with a round cross section. They ate everything in the Cretaceous ocean — stomachs of mosasaurs have yielded birds, bony fish, sharks, and smaller individuals of their own species. The holes in the ammonite shells from Montana are the same size as the teeth of medium-sized mosasaurs found in the same rock layers. But many of the holes are singular or not in a very convincing pattern.

Enter my eBay catch. The main holes form two slightly converging lines. Looks like the jaws of a mosasaur clamped down on the poor ammonite some

A mosasaur was a swimming relative of the Komodo dragon, only bigger. They grew to be up to 17.5 m long and had large pointy teeth with a round cross section.

74 million years ago. But the holes in one line are smaller than in the other line. Is this evidence against mosasaur attack? Are the boring limpets the real perpetrators?

 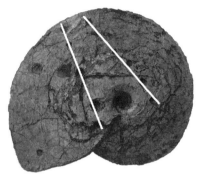

The ammonite *Placenticeras meeki* from the Cretaceous Bearpaw Formation, Telegraph Creek, Montana, USA, with and without white lines indicating the mosasaur jaws. Collection number PMO 227.613.

I think not, this is actually strong evidence for the mosasaur theory. The ammonite was not flattened when the bite came. The shell was a three-dimensional structure with the living chamber being more expanded than the inner whorls of the shell. And this is just what is shown on this specimen. The teeth are going deeper into the higher, expanded part and only slightly piercing the lower part.

But are all holes bite marks? Probably not. Perhaps it is a typical example of a Winnie-the-Pooh moment:

> *Rabbit said, 'Honey or condensed milk with your bread?'*
> [Pooh] *was so excited that he said, 'Both'...*
>
> A A Milne (1926) *Winnie-the-Pooh*

Fossil hunting with a six year old

Alex Cullum

I've heard many discouraging tales from people in recent years that have set out in search of good fossil finds and come home with pitifully little. It's true, more people are looking these days, so your competition is stiffer, but there are still good finds to be had, you just have to do your geological homework, research outcrops others might not visit, or be first on the beach on a low tide or after a good storm.

With this in mind I wasn't expecting to find much at Charmouth in Dorset, England, at the height of summer, but my six-year-old daughter Ella was pestering me to take her there and for once we were in the neighbourhood. Parking in the stone-cobbled car park and heading eastwards, over the River Char to the cliffs under Stonebarrow Hill, I recalled my visits with my parents as a kid. I was just five years old the first time I visited the Lyme Regis area and it's basically the reason why I'm a professional palaeontologist today. Dad always said, 'Find something you like doing, then look for someone stupid enough to pay you to do it.'

I can still feel the excitement of finding my first golden ammonites at Charmouth, and it's the same thrill I still get anywhere there are good specimens to be found. On a field trip a friend once remarked, 'You're usually such a nice guy, but you get so competitive when you're fossil hunting.' All I know is that it grabs me like nothing else and hours can pass in the blink of an eye, whether I'm finding anything good or not, the potential is always there.

'What are we looking for daddy?' asks Ella.

'Well we've got the Black Ven Marl Member here at the base of the cliff with the Belemnite Marl and Green Ammonite Mudstones Members above.'

'Not these then?' she asks, holding up a well-preserved irregular echinoid. I'd assumed it would be me finding the fossils, but it's a good first find.

'No, those are from the Cretaceous chalks west of Lyme Regis, much higher in the section.' Despite reading all about them in *The French Lieutenant's Woman* by John Fowles, I had never actually seen them here before.

'This whole section is from Early Jurassic marine environments, so we'll find pyritized ammonites, crinoids, and belemnites mainly. The cliffs are protected, but we're allowed to collect what we like from where the cliffs slump down onto the beach.'

'So is this more what you were expecting then daddy?' she asks, almost before my monolog on the Dorset stratigraphy is done. And she's holding out a small pyritized *Echioceras raricostatum* ammonite.

'That's exactly what we're after,' I say.

'And the belemnites are the pointy ones?' she asks.

'That's right,' I say. Twenty-five years of study and research and she's got all she needs from me in two sentences and thirty seconds at the location. I'm redundant and she's off down the beach ahead of me, stooping to pick up what's no doubt going to be an embarrassingly good selection of specimens by the time I can catch her up.

An hour later, she's covered the main area where the good stuff slumps down to be washed clean by each tide. I've found a few bits of crinoid, three small ammonites, and some belemnites (that I only picked up to show her really). But she's got a bag full of pyrite spirals and can't really be bothered to inspect my meagre collection. I guess my fossil-hunting days are over, but not due to the lack of specimens to find. I'm just too old and my eyesight isn't up to the competition.

Top left: Jurassic belemnite guards. Top right: Possible coprolite, or just a pyrite nodule. Lower images: *Echioceras raricostatum* ammonites, Charmouth, Dorset.

Gigantic Jurassic predators

Octávio Mateus

In popular culture, the Jurassic is synonymous with the dinosaurs but really the Mesozoic should, more fairly, be called the Era of Dinosaurs. The Mesozoic era stretched from about 252 to 66 million years ago — the Jurassic is the middle period of the Mesozoic (from 201 to 145 million years ago) after the Triassic and before the Cretaceous.

The history of life on Earth is a continuous succession of the rise and fall of animal species. Extinction is one of the most common events in life and it is a fact that most species that ever existed have gone extinct. Each genus of dinosaur had a limited time-span, about seven million years on average. Therefore, most Triassic species were already extinct in the Jurassic, and those of the Jurassic were gone by Cretaceous times.

The largest land predators during the Jurassic were the 150-million-year-old theropod dinosaur *Torvosaurus* (from North America and Portugal) and *Saurophaganax* (from North America). These animals were up to 12 m long and were the longest terrestrial meat-eaters for their times (Hendrickx & Mateus 2014). The famous *Tyrannosaurus rex* lived during the Cretaceous, about 80 million years later. This means that the Jurassic *Torvosaurus* had already been a fossil 80 million years before the famous *T. rex* roamed the earth.

Meanwhile, in the oceans

The oceans can support gigantic animals because buoyancy supports part of the body weight. This physical property and the productivity of the oceans enables the colossal gigantism in whales. The largest and heaviest animal that ever existed still lives today: the blue whale at 170 tonnes and up to 30 m in length. Curiously, the largest predator that ever existed also lives today: the sperm whale, at 56 tonnes and up to 20 m in length, that feeds mostly on giant squid.

During the Mesozoic, the oceans also held some giants. The largest during the Jurassic were the pliosaurs such as *Liopleurodon*, that could reach up to 12 m long. Pliosaurs were a group of plesiosaurs (marine reptiles); they were not dinosaurs, which were terrestrial only.

On land, the records for animal gigantism were in the past, as today, held by

The largest predator that ever existed
also lives today: the sperm whale.

plant-eaters: titanosaur sauropods such as *Argentinosaurus* and *Dreadnoughtus* during the Mesozoic, and the African elephant today.

Later, in the Cretaceous

The Cretaceous period saw the origin of some famous giant predators. The three largest ones were *Spinosaurus* from Africa, *Giganotosaurus* from South America, and *T. rex* in North America. The first was probably the longest (up to 17 m) while the last was among the most massive (up to 5000 kg).

Therefore, despite popular belief, *T. rex* was not the largest predator of the Jurassic:

- It lived during the Cretaceous period, not the Jurassic.
- The largest predators of the Jurassic were *Torvosaurus* and *Saurophaganax*.
- The largest land predator of all time was *Spinosaurus*.
- The largest predator of all time is the modern sperm whale.

References

Hendrickx, C and O Mateus (2014). *Torvosaurus gurneyi* n. sp., the largest terrestrial predator from Europe, and a proposed terminology of the maxilla anatomy in nonavian theropods. *PLoS ONE* **9**, e88905, 03 10.1371/journal.pone.0088905.

Go back to the collection

John de Vos

During 1891 and 1892 Eugène Dubois, searching for the missing link, found at Trinil (Java, Indonesia) a molar, which was ape-like, a skullcap, which had a cranial capacity between the apes and *Homo sapiens*, and a femur which was human-like. In 1894 he combined those fossils as *Pithecanthropus erectus* (now *Homo erectus*). Dubois excavated at Trinil for about 10 years, and besides these hominin fossils found a few thousand mammal and reptile fossils. In 1907 and 1908, Eleonora Selenka also excavated at Trinil and added a few more thousand fossils to the fauna.

At another Javan site, Kedung Brubus, Dubois found a mandible of his *Pithecanthropus erectus*. Here he excavated only a few hundred fossils. The whole collection from all the sites where Dubois excavated was sent to the Rijksmuseum van Natuurlijke Historie (now Naturalis Biodiversity Center), Leiden, The Netherlands, where it has been stored and curated since then. Sites with hominins are considered more special and important than sites without. For this reason, Trinil and Kedung Brubus have played a crucial role in the biostratigraphy of Java during the last century.

Dubois considered the faunas of the sites Trinil and Kedung Brubus as coeval, although he noticed a difference in faunal composition. This idea was adopted by researchers until the 1930s. Then the Dutch East Indies Geological Survey started a project to develop a biostratigraphy system for Java. One of their employers, the well-known Ralph von Koenigswald, came up with a scheme. Three faunas were distinguished by him for the Pleistocene of Java: Jetis (Early), Trinil (Middle), and Ngandong (Late Pleistocene) named after sites on Java.

When I started in the early 1980s as curator of the Dubois collection, I tried to understand the biostratigraphy of von Koenigswald. But his faunal list for Trinil was very long and I could not find the species in the Dubois or the Selenka collection. It turned out that von Koenigswald used locality names for his faunal successions, but the faunal assemblages differed from the fauna actually collected at those localities. According to von Koenigswald the 'Jetis' fauna was an assemblage of fossils from several localities, whereas the 'Trinil' fauna was an assemblage of fossils from Trinil, Kedung Brubus, and other sites. In this interpretation, the Kedung Brubus fauna was still coeval with Trinil.

However, checking the fauna from the type localities Trinil and Kedung Brubus in the Dubois collection showed that the Trinil fauna was poor in species, while the Kedung Brubus fauna had many more. In Trinil there was only one proboscidean, a *Stegodon*, while in Kedung Brubus there were two — a *Stegodon* and *Elephas*. Furthermore Kedung Brubus had a few more advanced species such as *Rhinoceros kendennindicus*, *Epileptobos*, and *Tapirus*, which were missing in Trinil. This bias was not caused by sampling error, because the Trinil collection contains a few thousand fossils and Kedung Brubus only a few hundred.

Ngandong		Ngandong	No *Duboisia*; more advanced forms
Trinil		Kedung Brubus	New arrivals of *Hyaena*, *Taprius*, *Epileptobos*, and *Elephas*
Jetis		Trinil	Poor in species; *Duboisia* and *Axis* are abundant

Figure adapted from Vos et al. 1982.

Based on the collections, the differences in the faunal composition of Trinil and Kedung Brubus are clear. As the sites are only a few kilometres from each other, an environmental explanation between the differences in fauna is not likely. So there must be a difference in age. Because of the absence of advanced species in Kedung Brubus, we concluded that Trinil is older.

Von Koenigswald used guide fossils for his units. In Jetis it was *Leptobos* (a bovid). However, this species was also present in Kedung Brubus. Based on this and other species which had Jetis and Kedung Brubus fauna in common, we concluded that Jetis was coeval with Kedung Brubus. This conclusion caused a debate about the absolute age (as a precise number of years) of the faunas and the *Homo erectus* specimens discussed here. There is still a debate about the absolute ages of these sites, while the biostratigraphic conclusion of the sequence of these events — the Trinil specimens being older than Kedung Brubus — is still considered to be correct.

What can we learn from this? Always go back to the collection from the type locality, and do not believe faunal lists.

References

Vos, J de, S Sartono, S Hardja-Sasmita, and P Sondaar (1982). The fauna from Trinil, type locality of *Homo erectus*; a reinterpretation. *Geologie en Mijnbouw* **61**, 207–211.

CURATION • BIOSTRATIGRAPHY • FIELDWORK

59

Golden graptolites

Alex Cullum & Denis Bates

Aberystwyth University in Wales, UK, is nicely located in the middle of a huge fossil-rich Palaeozoic basin. But I struggled as a poor undergraduate student with no car, to get to the best fossils sites in remote locations. So when Dr Denis Bates and Dr Dave Loydell took me and the first-year undergraduate class on our first fieldwork trip to the Rheidol Gorge, the fact that it was within biking distance from Aberystwyth marked it out as somewhere with special potential for me.

When we arrived at the dark, cleaved shale outcrops, deep in the beautiful green mossy gorge, Denis and Dave picked up a few specimens (David Attenborough style) as they explained about graptolites being branches of coral-like polyps called thecae which floated in the Silurian oceans some 440 million years ago. In locations first described by the great Welsh geologist Owen Thomas Jones (known as O T Jones) we found specimens of *Monograptus triangulatus*, which according to the monographs and range charts we had, proved this to be the Aeronian stage of the Early Llandovery. But unlike most locations where graptolites can be found as flat films, only visible when the light catches them from a certain angle, the specimens in the Rheidol Gorge are perfect 3D replicas of the original beasts in spellbinding pyrite gold.

Mesograptus magnus and *Monograptus triangulatus* (left) and *Petalolithus* (right) from the O T Jones locations.

The pyrite fills the thecae completely, and must have been precipitated before the sediment suffered any appreciable compaction, when the graptolites were buried by perhaps only a few centimetres of mud. The organic material of the graptolite has been carbonized, and is still present. On the inside of the graptolite thecae, the pyrite bears moulds of fibrils which were the overlapping bandage-like secretions that the organism used to construct its protective body walls.

O T Jones identified the potential importance of the Rheidol Gorge graptolite locations while mapping the Plynlimon–Ponterwyd area in the 1900s. Sixty years later, he returned there with members of the geology department — and he had total recall of the exposures. In the photograph he is shown in the Plynlimon area, discussing the geology with staff member Nancy Kirk (herself a legendary figure in Welsh geology and in research on graptolites). Detailed sedimentological and mapping work by Richard Cave from the British Geological Survey and graptolite biostratigraphy by David Loydell show how the outcrops within the Rheidol Gorge fit into the wider Silurian turbidite system of mid-Wales.

O T Jones and Nancy Kirk in the Plynlimon area Mid Wales, circa 1960. Credit: A S G Jones.

I returned to the gorge many times that year, but it was not until the following summer while researching my undergraduate thesis that I found and identified all the recognized species listed by Jones and subsequent researchers. To me the most beautiful forms were the broader genera *Diplograptus* and *Petalolithus*, where two strands of the rhabdosome (graptolite body) have their thecae zipped together. The few specimens I found of the delicate *Rastrites* — that look like fragile strips of eyelashes — always made me think of the spiky *Hallucigenia* creature from the Burgess Shale. In its way the Rheidol Gorge is a similarly special locality where the preservation of the fossils is truly unique.

Further reading

Cullum, A and D Loydell (2011). The Rhuddanian/Aeronian transition in the Rheidol Gorge, Mid Wales. *Proceedings of the Yorkshire Geological Society.* **58** (4), 261–266. ISSN 0044-0604.

Hardgrounds

Allard W Martinius

I still vividly remember the relaxed and beautiful day on the west coast of Malaysia, bathing in bright sunlight. We took a small boat to a recommended snorkelling spot along the coast of an island. I was prepared for the underwater beauty of coral reefs and colourful fishes, but I wasn't prepared for what I saw when I jumped into the water. I was actually overlooking something very similar to a subtropical 53-million-year-old shallow-water and wave-dominated hardground environment, complete with the same fauna that occurred in the sediment-starved areas of the Early Eocene Roda fan delta! The morphologies of the wave-resistant lobate coral colonies were exactly the same, the thick-walled shallow-burrowing bivalves looked very similar, and the many turriform, turbinoform, and conical gastropods together with the spiny echinoids completed the image. Amazing.

Shortly before this trip, I had finished my master's degree looking at the fauna–substrate relationships of the hardgrounds found on top of some of the large, rapidly deposited sandstone bodies in the Roda Formation of the Spanish Pyrenees. An exciting topic that I had pursued as if I was Sherlock Holmes trying to reconstruct an ancient scene of rise to, and subsequent fall from, glory. I had used some modern and some old-fashioned, but still effective, techniques to collect data, develop the palaeoenvironmental model, and decipher the relationship with sediment dispersal patterns over time. Some of it was straightforward, but much of it had to be deduced and interpreted. Sudden shifts in the locus of sand deposition happened frequently and had a profound impact on the palaeoecological conditions locally causing the gradual development or, contrarily, rapid cessation of richly populated invertebrate palaeocommunities.

On the hardgrounds, the abundantly occurring fossil *Goniaraea* coral colonies are generally well preserved, and over the years the many visitors to these parts of the Roda outcrops have significantly reduced their surviving number. (Which, by the way, is a plea to field-trip participants to better protect outcrops!) Rays, sharks, and sea turtles patrolled the waters, and the various Eocene *Conus* species so commonly occurring on the hardgrounds were likely as venomous then as they are today. Colour, though, was the one striking feature that was missing: the preserved Roda hardground fossils are uninspiringly brownish

Why does palaeontology never cease to
fascinate me? It is the sheer beauty and intricacy
of past ecosystems and their diversity…

grey. So, when I dipped my head beneath the waves near the Malaysian island the transformation was complete. I was relocated back in time — not using a DeLorean, but a small motor boat.

Why does palaeontology never cease to fascinate me? It is the sheer beauty and intricacy of past ecosystems and their diversity, the interdependency and interactions of the physical environment, and the biological adaptations to it. It is the understanding and comprehension of why that particular ecosystem ceased to exist, what the factors were that controlled it, and what we can deduce from it that might have meaning for our current environments. I am excited by the view through a 'window to a past world' that is much larger and more multidimensional than my own life observations and experiences allow. I find it intriguing to realize that environmental conditions may change — gradually or dramatically — but that life will return and continue albeit in different ways and forms.

Relatively sudden and high-impact environmental changes are common in life's history. Maybe we should be reassured that, from an ecological point of view, we don't need to feel despair about the environmental calamities and challenges we are facing. Which brings me back to the fascinating life forms, their mutual dependencies and interactions with the physical environment, and the Malaysian island — there to be enjoyed and cherished.

How dinosaur tracks were made

Michael Romano

Dinosaur tracks preserved in rocks are the fossilized remains of any behavioural activity of the living animal. Thus, in the case of dinosaurs, they may be the imprints of their feet on the substrate, the outline of their body as they lay on the ground, or the drag mark of a tail. We may also find more peripheral things such as skin imprints, nests, or even eggs. These tracks and traces are valuable indicators of the animal's actual body shape, particularly with respect to their feet, since bones are just the skeletal support and generally lack the soft tissue.

In any one day an animal may potentially make thousands of footprints (in one normal working day I made 5243 footsteps!). But of course few will be preserved. The simplest scenario for track formation is for an animal to make an impression on a yielding substrate (such as mud) and leave a negative imprint (mould) on the surface. This would later be infilled with a layer of sediment, such as sand. After lithification (hardening) and wearing away of the mud (now mudstone) the resulting print would be a positive cast on the underside of the (now) sandstone. Other sediment types and more complicated processes may be involved — but the principle is essentially the same. If the print is buried and preserved without modification by later water or wind currents this type of print would produce the most accurate representation of the foot shape, so-called *elite* prints which are not modified or superimposed by later prints (Lockley & Hunt 1995). Variations of the process include underprints and transmitted prints (Thulborn 1990; Romano & Whyte 2003). Both of these types result in prints which usually show less detail than elite prints, or in the case of the transmitted prints even exaggerate the foot size.

How do we recognize whether or not these hieroglyphs in the rocks are dinosaur prints? Most bipedal dinosaurs (those that habitually walked on two legs) had three functional toes. If there were other toes, these rarely made marks in the sediment as they were too small or too far above the ground. So any mark in the rocks with three radiating imprints are good candidates. We can take this further. If the three digit imprints are quite strongly divergent, pad-like, and lack well-marked claw imprints then the tracks are probably representative of a herbivorous dinosaur (such as iguanodontids or hadrosaurs). Less divergent, slimmer digit imprints with distinct claw marks indicate a carnivorous type (the 'raptors' of *Jurassic Park*). By applying work done on living animals we can also estimate the hip height of these bipeds. Using the formula $h = 4FL$, where h

Sauropod pes (hind foot) from the Middle Jurassic of the Yorkshire coast, England.

is hip height and *FL* is footprint length, we can estimate the size of the animal. Although this is a useful first approximation, other estimates of hip height for bipeds have varied from 4.5 to 5.9 times the footprint length.

Quadrupedal dinosaur tracks tend to be dominated by prints of the giant sauropods *Diplodocus* and *Brachiosaurus*. These prints, often up to 1 m across, are subrounded to subtriangular in outline, often with 3 to 5 short toe digits. However, size is not absolutely critical in determining whether the structure is a print, since animal types and ages result in a wide range of print size.

As with body fossils, we apply names to distinct print shapes, based on the binomial Linnaean system we adopt for modern and fossil animals and plants. Understandably there is some opposition to this system, since we are dealing with traces not organisms and one animal may make a number of different traces (depending on whether it was running, crawling, or even jumping), each with a different name. To clarify the distinction between species and trace fossil names, we prefix the latter with 'ichnos' (from the Greek meaning track or trace) with each name consisting of an ichnogenus and ichnospecies.

Finally it is a fact, though perhaps initially bemusing, that although dinosaur tracks may be extremely abundant in the fossil record, they are usually not associated with the remains of the maker's bones. This is also true of tracks and trails of other vertebrate, and indeed invertebrate, animals. Sufficient to say that, in the case of dinosaurs that lived in terrestrial environments, the conditions were not conducive to their skeletons being preserved in the fossil record. So, in the absence of bones, the answers lie in the tracks.

References

Lockley, M and A Hunt (1995). *Dinosaur tracks and other fossil footprints of the western United States.* Columbia, 338 p.

Romano, M and M Whyte (2003). Jurassic dinosaur tracks… *Proceedings of the Geological Society of Yorkshire*, **54**, 185–21.

Thulborn, T (1990). *Dinosaur Tracks.* Chapman and Hall, London, 410 p.

How dinosaurs walked

Michael Romano

Bones may be indispensable in the reconstruction of an animal; but are of less use in providing evidence of what an animal was actually doing in everyday life. The traces and tracks left by dinosaurs going about their business is what brings the skeletons to life. Herds moving at different speeds, hunts, stampedes, and even limping dinosaurs have all been documented in fossil tracks.

Most dinosaurs spent much of their time walking. Trackways provide information on the speed and direction the animals were moving, as well as their posture — the angles at which they held their limbs. Unlike lizards, dinosaurs were not sprawlers, they did not hold their legs out sideways at nearly 90 degrees to their bodies. In fact bipedal dinosaurs (who walked on their two rear legs) produced nearly straight trackways with their hind limbs held nearly vertical and tucked in to their sides.

Other gaits, besides walking, have also been recognized in trackways made by bipedal dinosaurs. Using the stride length SL, the distance between two successive left or right footprints, and hip height h which is approximated as four times the footprint length, and using the ratio SL/h or *relative stride length*, it is possible to estimate whether the dinosaur was walking ($SL/h < 2.0$) or running ($SL/h > 2.9$). These values are based on those observed in modern terrestrial vertebrates.

It is possible to take this investigation further, and estimate the actual speed the dinosaur was moving. A number of formulas have been proposed to determine the absolute speed V of dinosaurs from their trackways. Among the most commonly used equation is that proposed by Alexander (1976) as follows (where g is due to gravity):

$$V = 0.25g^{0.5} \, SL^{1.67} \, h^{-1.17}$$

It comes as no surprise that the majority of speeds calculated from trackways show that most dinosaurs spent their days walking — perhaps feeding or migrating — at speeds of between 4 and 8 km/h (Thulborn 1990). Rarely, speeds of up to 40 km/h have been documented for bipedal theropods. The gaits of quadrupedal dinosaurs (sauropods, stegosaurs, ankylosaurs) are not so readily analysed as those of the bipeds, in part due to the structure of their shoulder girdle that may inhibit stride length of the forelimb and their frequently longer hind limb.

Footprint rotation, or the angle that the long axis of the footprint makes with the median axis of the trackway, provides further evidence of the style in which the dinosaurs moved their limbs. Examples of both positive and negative rotation are known, and reflect the varying gaits adopted by different dinosaur groups.

Finally, the record of tracks of swimming dinosaurs may at first appear contradictory since a swimming animal will not leave traces in the sediment. However, animals taking off from a river bank, or occasionally hitting the bottom sediment in fairly shallow water do leave scratch marks in the sediment. These tracks may be differentiated from normal footprints by the parallel nature of the digit imprints as they were dragged through the sediment; contrasting with the more typical radiating digit imprints left by a walking or running animal. Scenarios of animals swimming in floods against the current have been recorded from the Middle Jurassic of the Yorkshire coast (Whyte & Romano 2001).

In short, virtually every type of locomotion may be preserved in the fossil record; except flying!

A swimming print of the hind foot of a tridactyl bipedal dinosaur, from the Middle Jurassic of the Yorkshire coast, England. Note the three slightly curved subparallel traces made as the foot digits were dragged through the sediment. The length of the print is approximately 30 cm.

References

Alexander, R McN (1976). Estimates of speeds of dinosaurs. *Nature*, **261**, 129–130.

Thulborn, T (1990). *Dinosaur Tracks*. Chapman and Hall, London, 410 p.

Whyte, M A and M Romano (2001). A dinosaur ichnocoenosis from the Middle Jurassic of Yorkshire, UK. *Ichnos*, **8**, 223–234.

Ichnology and the minor phyla

S George Pemberton

Perhaps one of the most frustrating — and most fascinating — facets of ichnology is the attempt to establish the zoological affinities of specific ichnofossils. It has been pointed out that difficulties arise in any systematic classification of ichnofossils, partly because extensive comparisons of trace morphology and ethology with the traces of most modern organisms has not yet been made. Furthermore, ichnofossils mostly reflect the behaviour of animals, and only to a small extent reflect their anatomy or morphology. The result is that more than one genus or species of ichnofossil may have been constructed by a single species of animal, or conversely, different species of animals may have made identical species or genera of trace fossils. For example, *Skolithos linearis* at one locality may show affinities to the phoronids, whereas at another locality they may show affinities to onuphid polychaetes.

Trace fossils record the activities of benthic organisms, many of which are soft-bodied and are not readily preserved. This less preservable group includes entire phyla (such as the nemerteans, nematodes, nematomorphs, annelids, sipunculids, echiurans, pognophorans, priapulids, phoronids, onychoporids, urochordates, nemertinids, chaetognathids, cephalochordates, and enteropneusts) or classes (i.e. anthozoans, aplacophorans, holothuroids, and demosponges). Many of these lineages are diverse (i.e. at present there are 18 000 extant species of annelids, 15 000 species of nematodes, 900 species of nemerteans, 2000 species of urochordates, and 320 species of sipunculids) and many are known to have originated at the start of the Phanerozoic. For example, annelids, echurians, pognophorans, priapulids, phoronids, onychoporids, and enteropneusts are known from deposits as old as Cambrian.

These groups are known from Konservat-Lagerstätten — exceptional preservational cases, where the soft parts of organisms are preserved as impressions — for example the Lower Cambrian Chengjiang fauna Qiongzhusi Formation (The Maotianshan Shale) of China, the Middle Cambrian Burgess Shale in British Columbia, the Upper Cambrian Orsten fauna of Sweden, the Lower Ordovician Fezouata Formation of Morocco, and the Lower Devonian Hunsrück Slate of Germany, among others. Traditionally, however, palaeontologists have relegated such groups to 'minor phyla' status and have ignored them in the following ways:

Ichnofossils mostly reflect the behaviour of animals,
and only to a small extent reflect their anatomy or morphology.

1. The analysis of diversity trends through time.
2. The taphonomic implications of the 'incomplete fossil record'.
3. The evolution of infaunal suspension and deposit feeders.
4. The periodicity of mass extinctions.
5. The interpretation of population strategies.

The ichnological record of these minor phyla can have considerable significance. For example, *Treptichnus pedum* is regarded as the earliest widespread complex trace fossil. Its appearance is contemporaneous with the last of the Ediacaran biota and defines the dividing line between the Ediacaran and Cambrian Periods. Dzik (2005, 2007) has compared structures of Cambrian priapulids known from the Burgess Shale and the Chengjiang mudstones with horizontal burrows and bilobate traces and concluded that *Treptichnus pedum* was produced by priapulids. Likewise, during experimental ichnological studies with modern priapulids Vannier et al. (2010) were able to show that typical serial burrows of treptichnids were most probably produced by priapulids during shallow probing for infaunal or epifaunal prey.

We need a better understanding of the ichnological record of the so-called minor phyla that are not otherwise preserved in the usual shelly and bony fossil record. They can offer a more complete record of ancient biodiversity and behaviour, thereby enabling a better reconstruction of the palaeoecology of ancient aquatic communities.

References

Dzik, J (2005). Behavioral and anatomical unity of the earliest burrowing animals and the cause of the 'Cambrian explosion'. *Paleobiology* **31**, 507–525.

Dzik, J (2007). The Verdun Syndrome: simultaneous origin of protective armour and infaunal shelters at the Precambrian–Cambrian transition. In Vickers-Rich, P and Komarower, P (eds.) *The Rise and fall of the Ediacaran Biota*. Special publications **286**, Geological Society, London, 405-414.

Vannier, J, I Calandra, C Gaillard, and A Zylinska (2010). Priapulid worms: Pioneer horizontal burrowers at the Precambrian-Cambrian boundary. *Geology* **38**, 711–714.

Into the mouth of the mouse

Lars van den Hoek Ostende

I was nearing graduation and eating lunch in the canteen of our institute with my supervisor, who at that time was getting close to retirement. Pasting his bread with marmalade, he looked at me pensively. 'You know Lars, at breakfast my children said something that made me think.' He took a bite, carefully considering how to continue. 'Do you realize that it is actually strange that we devote our lives to looking at rodent molars?'

Of course, his children were right. If you aim to impress an attractive stranger at the bar about being a palaeontologist, you better start rambling about dinosaurs. 'Leading specialist in the taxonomy of Miocene hedgehogs' will not cut it. As a student, I even once vowed that I would never waste my time on something as obscure as mice teeth. But it only took a three-week lab to convince me that they are really cool, and I have been addicted ever since.

So what is so nice about the teeth of mice? There are a few things you need to know first. The molars of small mammals are very typical: you can identify the species by looking only at the teeth. They are very tough, and so they preserve well and in great numbers. And because teeth are used to eat (!), you immediately know something about their diet. In short, there is a lot of information in these tiny objects, which are usually just 1 mm long.

The fun starts at collecting. The public perception of palaeontological excavations is a bunch of people lying on the ground, carefully brushing sediment from a bone. It makes great television, but does not show the cramped knees, the sunburn, or the hungover student peering over your shoulder. Having endured all that, at the end of the day you are lucky if you have recovered one fossil.

We don't use toothbrushes, at least not for excavating. The tools of the trade are a pick-axe, a shovel, and a stack of bags. The hard work lies in gathering clay from a fossiliferous layer, and putting it out to dry. After that, the sieving starts. You get to play with mud and water all day long. It takes you back to kindergarten, but this time you actually get paid to do it. And once everything is processed, you can end up with hundreds of fossils.

It is that sheer quantity that is the real trick. You don't study a single fossil (I feel very sorry for palaeoanthropologists), but an entire fauna at once. If you

Each collection of small mammal molars gives another glimpse

of the landscape in a time long gone. I am looking at

rodent teeth, but I am studying a changing world.

have various fossiliferous levels in one hillside, you can see the morphological changes as individual lineages evolve, and clear changes in the composition of the fauna which reflect the changes in the environment. Flying squirrels disappear from the record as the forest gives way to plains; beavers appear when the climate turns moist. Each collection of small mammal molars gives another glimpse of the landscape in a time long gone. I am looking at rodent teeth, but I am studying a changing world.

Of course, it is always good to be reminded that the object of your studies is a little out of the ordinary — whether it is by your kids, the stranger at the bar, or even the manager who thinks that palaeontology is only about dinosaurs. But the story fossil mice have to tell is an intriguing tale. Apart from that, there is also the practical side to things. At least I'll never strain myself lifting one of my fossils.

Lentic jeff and other bugs

Andrew R Bowman

Biostratigraphy is a specialized niche within the petroleum industry. I would venture to claim that it is the most specialized discipline within this diverse industry. Perhaps this is why biostratigraphy (and palaeontology in general) is not well understood by most of our non-biostratigrapher colleagues. This misunderstanding led to the nicknames of Bug Guy/Bug Boy — and I assume Bug Gal/Bug Girl although I have never heard these names used — given to us by non-biostratigraphers (e.g. drilling engineers, geophysicists, etc.), and creative shorthand nomenclature given to various species and useful biostratigraphic events (e.g. Rob E, Big hum, Cib carst, etc). Much of this informal but unique nomenclature was created and adopted several decades ago by companies exploring the US Gulf Coast, and many of these biostratigraphic schemes or zonations have since been published or otherwise formalized among the petroleum companies. The role of the Bug People in trying to decipher the many amusing biostratigraphic names I think is worthy of mention.

The history of palaeontology in the energy industry dates back to the early 1920s, when most major petroleum companies were employing palaeontologists to create subsurface well correlations. Around this time (early to mid 1920s), the first biostratigraphy related publications began appearing in petroleum geology journals and this exposure aided in the establishment of biostratigraphy as a crucial discipline and tool within the petroleum industry of the Gulf Coast. Throughout the decades, staff in the many oil companies constructed unique biostratigraphic names and codes for the primary events being used as stratigraphic horizons and applied to the correlation of key reservoir intervals. As the taxonomy of foraminifera was well understood at the onset of Gulf Coast hydrocarbon exploration, they became the primary microfossil group used for biostratigraphy in relatively shallow water environments and across the continental shelf of the Gulf of Mexico. As a result, many of the abbreviated and interesting biostratigraphic events focused around species of foraminifera. As these unique monikers were derived by internal staff, each company had their own in-house biostratigraphic scheme. So the same biostratigraphic event usually had several different aliases, which ensured many years of confusion.

As well reports were shared through partnerships (for example on field development projects), geologists became aware of the excessive variation among horizon names and reservoir units. In the mid-1980s, to further trouble and complicate the issue, as a result of falling oil prices the number of internal staff biostratigraphers within the major petroleum companies was drastically reduced. This period marked a frenzy of employment activity among industry biostratigraphers, as most former staff biostratigraphers sought careers in the consulting realm. Several major petroleum companies maintained at least one staff biostratigrapher to act as de-coder of the various biostratigraphic schemes, but staff were primarily responsible for coordinating projects for consultants, performing quality control on biostratigraphic interpretations of various data-sets, and providing some degree of internal stratigraphic support.

When performing project work or wellsite support, a consultant would, naturally enough, apply the unique biostratigraphic scheme that he or she used or helped create while internally employed at an oil company. The influx of consultants following this work model during the mid-1980s to late 1990s ensured complete disorder and confusion within the Gulf of Mexico biostratigraphic nomenclature and Gulf of Mexico-related biostratigraphy. Thankfully the Gulf Coast Taxonomic Equivalency Project was created in 1999 to help with the clean-up of existing foraminifera-based biostratigraphic nomenclature throughout the region. The main result of this work was a taxonomic synonym table, which to this day allows incoming staff biostratigraphers to work more efficiently and relatively pain-free.

Since the 1990s, hydrocarbon exploration has advanced further into the deep-water Gulf of Mexico. The enhanced usefulness and biostratigraphic superiority of calcareous nannofossils became evident when drilling these deepwater wells. Fortunately (or unfortunately, depending on which side you are on), species of calcareous nannofossils were not typically renamed or abbreviated by non-biostratigraphers. This may be because species names within the group are not as easy to nickname, or maybe the times of creative naming had passed. Regardless, the calcareous nannofossil species that were abbreviated are amusing, but the foraminifera names possess the most entertainment value.

Calcareous nannofossils

Disco A	*Discoaster quinqueramus*	Cat mex	*Catinaster mexicanus*
Cat coal	*Catinaster coalitus*	Cocco mio	*Coccolithus miopelagicus*

Foraminifera

Tex mex	*Textularia mexicana*	Big A	*Bigenerina floridana*
Amph E	*Amphistegina lessoni*	Cib carst	*Cibicides carstensi*
Tex W	*Textularia stapperi*	Big hum	*Bigenerina humblei*
Cib op	*Cibicides opima*	Amph B	*Amphistegina chipolensis*
Gyro 6	*Gyroidina cf altispira*	Marg A	*Marginulina ascensionensis*
Siph davisi	*Siphonina davisi*	Lentic jeff	*Lenticulina jeffersonensis*

Life took off in the Ediacaran
Emily Mitchell

There has been life on earth for over three billion years, but for most of this time it consisted of microbes with limited diversity. Most modern phyla suddenly appeared in the fossil record 542 million years ago. For many years the so-called Cambrian explosion was thought to be the start of complex macroscopic life on earth. However, we now know that complex macroscopic life appeared before that, during the Ediacaran (635–542 Ma).

Ediacaran ecosystems were very different to those of the Cambrian. Microbial mats formed the foundation of the ecosystem, providing a stabilizing base on which the Ediacaran species could live. These microbial mats also helped preserve fossils of the soft-bodied organisms: bacterial precipitation of iron sulphide cemented sediments around dead and decaying organisms, forming a 'death mask' which resulted in exceptional preservation. Furthermore, because movement was limited during the Ediacaran, there are hundreds of bedding planes where almost entire ecosystems were preserved. Some of the oldest Ediacaran macrofossil bedding planes preserved thousands of specimens under volcanic ash, often to sub-millimetre detail, providing a unique window into these ancient ecosystems, which is unprecedented anywhere else in the fossil record.

On top of the microbial mats grew many exotic organisms, some up to 2 m long, with body plans so unique they are difficult to place on the tree of life. Some species such as the mollusc-like *Kimberella* may have been one of the first animals, others such as *Thectardis* might have been a sponge. Others, such as *Charnia*, had a fractal branching structure in which each branch has many sub-branches, a body plan unique to the Ediacaran.

During the Ediacaran we see a number of key innovations, including movement, burrowing, and the consumption of other organisms. Most of the oldest Ediacaran macrofossils were incapable of movement, but some later bedding planes show trace fossils similar to those made by cnidiarians, suggesting some species were capable of movement. Younger beds contain strong evidence of undermat burrowing. *Yorgia* has several instances where there are body impressions in the microbial mat, which then end in a body fossil, as though the organism has flopped forward. It is thought the organisms may have been feeding off the

A close-up view of one of the key Ediacaran localities: 'E' surface, Mistaken Point, Newfoundland, Canada (565 Ma). At the top right, various frondose organisms including Charniodiscus can be seen, while a cluster of Fractofusus can be seen at the bottom left, exhibiting the multiple levels of branching. This community lived in deep water, and is thought to have lived off dissolved organic carbon found in the water column.

microbial mat, absorbing nutrients through their undersides. Other body fossils, such as *Kimberella* have been found near concentric scratch marks in the microbial mat, suggesting they were eating at the mat. Closer to the Cambrian we see species such as *Cloudinia*, a reef-builder which is thought to have biomineralized as a defence against predation, as evidenced by the presence of boreholes in some shells.

Despite the fact that the Ediacaran macrofossils occur during such a key transition of life on earth, there are still many fundamental unanswered questions: While the phylogenetic affinity of some species is fairly well resolved (e.g. *Kimberella*), many — including the oldest fractally branching rangeomorphs — are still unknown. Furthermore, there are only two possible Ediacaran species that survived into the Cambrian, but it is not known yet whether the lack of Ediacaran survivors is due to an absence of preservation conditions, a mass extinction, or a slow dying-off as the Ediacaran macrobiota were replaced by their Cambrian counterparts.

Ediacaran macrofossils and their ecosystems represent the start of complex life on earth. Because of this, understanding the Ediacaran, and attempting to answer these key questions, is key to understanding animal evolution and the development of life on our planet.

Museums matter

Giles Miller

Ask a biostratigrapher where they would normally start their research and I would wager that very few of them would say 'in a museum'. But museums play a key role in palaeontology and biostratigraphy and to illustrate this I have put together 10 reasons why they matter.

1. **Types.** Museums hold the specimens that define fossil species, the building blocks for biostratigraphic schemes. The holotype specimens are usually the most important but specimen repositories can contain a range of relevant specimens and samples from the type sections where these species are defined.

2. **Age range.** Museums contain comparative examples of the same species that can help to define the stratigraphic distribution, and provide reference points for #5.

3. **Geographical ranges.** As well as defining the time periods for which a relevant species is present, museum collections can help with evaluating the geographical distribution of species. Widespread species make the best biostratigraphic markers.

4. **Environmental ranges.** The environmental distribution of a species can be evaluated by comparing with other materials, whether that be other fossils of known environmental range, or samples that can be studied for comparative material. The best biostratigraphic markers are usually marine species, or are found in a wide range of environments so that their stratigraphic ranges are not significantly affected by environmental changes.

5. **Evolutionary changes.** Combining details of stratigraphic age, geographical and environmental distribution, allows interpretations of evolutionary lineages.

6. **Reference for collecting more material.** Museum collections can be a great pointer for future fieldwork to inform biostratigraphic research. I know of several successful major grant applications that resulted from finding exceptionally preserved material in museum collections and proposing fieldwork to collect more material.

7. **Archives of material from localities that no longer exist.** Some collecting sites no longer exist as they have become overgrown or have been covered

over during construction work for buildings, roads, or rail lines. Museums provide a way to preserve data from such sites.

8. **Destructive analysis is possible.** Comparative samples are sometimes available to reprocess and provide details of assemblages related to specific material. Occasionally destructive geochemical studies on museum samples can provide further information about environments or ages. Museums have their own policies on sample analysis — many allow isotope studies, for example.

9. **Archives of previous studies.** Archiving collections in museums is a way for scientists to validate their work or allow re-interpretation in the light of future research.

10. **Easily available online resources.** Most museums now provide online records: usually information relating to collection, acquisition, and identification of items. Increasingly, images of important taxa are also being made available.

These are all good reasons for using museum collections in palaeontological and biostratigraphic research. So what is preventing scientists from using these collections? Are there misconceptions? Are researchers aware that sometimes sample material is available for restudy or that destructive techniques can be applied to museum specimens to release important information about them? Perhaps the wealth of freely available electronic publications featuring high-quality images of biostratigraphically important taxa render referring to type materials unnecessary?

I am a museum curator so it is no surprise that I advocate the use of museum collections. However, I also believe that the responsibility of ensuring that people use the collections lies with those who manage them. Providing information and images online to researchers, advocating the collections, and facilitating access are important ways forward.

Never ignore the bits you don't recognize

Haydon Bailey

When visiting restaurants abroad, it's always worth trying something you don't recognize on the menu, because it could be really good. The same is true when working through a micropalaeontological sample… there could be bits and pieces in there that you don't recognize straight away, but they could prove to be very useful. Items listed as *incertae sedis* always leave you wondering what they might be and how they might fit in to the story.

For several years micropalaeontologists logged 'pink, calcareous spheres' from North Sea Upper Cretaceous Chalk sections. Persistence established that these were calcitized *Cenosphaera radiolaria*, occurring within one of three isochronous red chalk events (Early Campanian, Mid Santonian, or Early Coniacian). Each of these represents a warm, oxygenated water mass influx into the basin on the eastern margin of the opening North Atlantic. Each event has an associated abundance of planktonic foraminifera and age-constrained calcareous nannoplankton allowing precise age assignment as well as a palaeoenvironmental interpretation. A fourth red chalk event occurs at the top of the Late Campanian interval, characterized by a distinctive planktonic foraminifera traceable around the North Atlantic and into Tethyan sections, including the Campanian–Maastrichtian stage boundary type section at Tercis, France.

When logging through thin sections of carbonates, it's easy to ignore fragments of bioclastic debris which are not immediately recognizable. A typical overlooked item could be fragmented echinoderm debris. It's easy to recognize an echinoid spine in thin section because of the distinctive ribbing or floral cross section; however it's not so easy to pick out more irregular rhomboid echinoid plate fragments. After a search you start to recognize that they frequently reveal their internal calcite crystal structure by having minute crystals of pyrite on crystal boundaries. They will vary in the amount of pyrite growth, but it's always the echinoids which show pyritization first, allowing them to be distinguished from other bioclastic debris.

It's questionable why you might want to count echinoid debris in thin sections, but in very shallow-water carbonates, where there is often a restricted microfauna, pulses of echinoid debris appear to coincide with minor flooding events and these may provide a key to the environmental controls on sea level in the area. It's difficult to know accurately what sort of echinoid numbers may be present in a sample when you consider that a single *Ophiura albida* Forbes (brittle star) comprises a total of 4966 individual calcite plates (yes — they have been counted), but when you're dealing with regular pulses in abundance then these may be significant.

The most critical ability for a micropalaeontologist today is the power of observation, followed closely by the need to record accurately what has been observed. Recognition and identification are secondary as long as you can recall what you found and where you found it.

Nothing is sacred

Martin Brasier

One of my pleasures is to remind people that reading any part of the fossil record is rather like taking part in a game of cards. Consider, for example, the following four competing hands: Q,Q,Q,Q / 6,7,8,9 / A,2,3,4 / 2,3,5,8. Our task here is to guess which is the winning hand. But have we got the right number of cards? And what game is actually being played? Our challenge has been to guess the name of the game.

Questioning our assumptions

So when have we been provided with the wrong cards or guessed at the wrong game? Where might we have been going wrong over the last few decades? Happily, my own research field is ripe with charming examples. Here is a list of some of my favourite seriously mistaken concepts relating to the history of life in deep time. I am happy to confess to being adjunct to some of these debates myself over the decades (Brasier 2009, 2012). So moving backwards in the manner of a Time Traveller from modern to ancient, here are some questionable guesses at gambits in life's great game:

1. **Were mass extinctions caused by large environmental perturbations?** This was popular in the 1980s but now looks highly misleading. Large perturbations could conceivably have caused the timing, but arguably not the magnitude of extinctions. Magnitude is likely related to the state and connectedness of the ecosystem itself. That means it is the conditions before a mass extinction — and the interconnectedness of the ecosystem — that now deserve our understanding. In short, we need a systems approach to the fossil record.

2. **Was the Cambrian explosion an explosion of fossils rather than of body plans?** This idea has been popular in recent decades, but no longer looks sustainable on geological evidence: the high quality of preservation in the Neoproterozoic — almost wherever we look — fails to show fossil signs of a very deep ancestry. We are starting to realize that fossilization has evolved. And the Cambrian explosion was real.

3. **Does the Ediacara biota actually preserve the ancestors of Cambrian animals?** This was orthodoxy until the 1990s, but few now accept this — except for the last few million years, where some precursors may have emerged. Instead, we must accept a much more interesting concept — that the rules

Science is a unique system for the measurement
of doubt. Nothing is sacred.

for functional morphology (and hence for morphospace) were different before the advent of the through-gut circa 545 Ma. My hunch is that the evolution of the gut plus symbiotic microbes, revolutionized ecosystems and changed the nature of biogeochemical cycling. We therefore need to explore co-evolutionary processes in deep time.

4. **Did eukaryotes largely evolve in the sea?** Maybe. Maybe not. We know so little about the non-marine fossil record in the Boring Billion. But we are now discovering a surprisingly diverse biota, including eukaryotic algae, in one-billion-year-old lakes. Indeed, there are biological reasons for suspecting much of the evolution of green algae, cyanobacteria, and maybe even life itself could have taken place away from the sea. There is therefore a need to check out all manner of unexplored habitats, to fill in our missing fossil record. We need to challenge our long-entrenched assumptions about evolutionary habitat.

5. **Was oxygenic photosynthesis present in the early Archaean?** Few are willing to accept this now. The Apex chert 'microfossils' (3.46 Ga) are now sadly dismissed (by myself and other researchers) as inorganic mineral growths that formed over eons in a hydrothermal vein system. Cyanobacteria are now thought to have evolved up to a billion years later, and even then they barely take on their familiar modern forms. This reminds us of the wider point that we must not shoehorn ancient structures into modern groups. Early organisms often differ from those we would expect to find. Think of Jurassic dinosaurs, Ordovician graptolites, Cambrian anomalocardids, or Ediacaran rangeomorphs. Fossils do it differently.

A final word of advice. Remember that science is not a belief system. Science is a unique system for the measurement of doubt. Nothing is sacred. And certainly not the words of an Oxford professor. Oh, and I nearly forgot. The winning hand was, of course, 2,3,5,8. (Fibonacci series: self-similarity, growth stability, multicellularity.)

Reference

Brasier, M (2009). *Darwin's Lost World: the hidden history of animal life.* Oxford University Press. 304 p.

Brasier, M (2012). *Secret Chambers: the inside story of complex life.* Oxford University Press. 256 p.

Our core skill

Mike Bowman

The application of detailed and expert analysis of plant and animal microfossils — spores, pollen, dinoflagellates, foraminifera, and other groups — is an essential element of describing the subsurface for the upstream oil and gas industry. In areas of complex geology with challenging drilling conditions, both in the overburden and at the surface, the value of real-time (wellsite) biostratigraphic analysis is often an essential prerequisite for safe and successful drilling operations. On many occasions in my career I would not have felt safe to embark upon drilling activities without my trusty biostratigrapher watching every inch of key sections of the well.

The value of the biostratigrapher is also unquestioned in the creation of a regional- to reservoir-scale framework to assess a petroleum system or reservoir. They provide essential data for everything from regional exploration to prospect evaluation in the exploration stages of the business. In reservoir appraisal, development, and production the impact of having a reliable high-resolution correlation framework for managing reservoir sweep, well placement, and recovery efficiency can be profound and often not intuitive.

I worry deeply about the gradual and ongoing demise of this critical area of applied petroleum geoscience. Many of the historically successful master's programs and research groups are closing or are already consigned to the past (Bailey & Jones 2012). There is a real shortfall in this core skill and an equally worrying senior-skewed demographic profile to the existing population of experts. In an era of computer-based, button-pushing geoscience it is all too easy to overlook such niche areas of expertise; we must value, sustain, and nurture these specialist disciplines not only to educate the non-specialist geoscientists but also to create the future micropalaeontologists and palynologists. Only specialists will support the business with new knowledge and understanding from original research.

In the UK, the recent creation of a NERC- and industry-sponsored Centre for Doctoral Training in oil and gas recognizes the need for greater investment in subsurface skills and capability for the North Sea and wider. Hopefully as the Centre develops and evolves, we will see applied microbiostratigraphy becoming a core part of the resulting research — albeit a highly specialised part. If you

I would not have felt safe to embark upon drilling activities without my trusty biostratigrapher watching every inch of key sections of the well.

thumb through the proceedings of the Petroleum Geology of Northwest Europe conferences during the 1980s and 90s, or many of the petroleum geoscience related special publications of the Geological Society of London, one cannot fail to recognize the fundamental influence that applied biostratigraphic palynology and micropalaeontology has had upon realizing value from the North Sea asset base. If we are to be successful in creating future value from those remaining pools, yet-to-find barrels, new plays, and stranded resources, applied biostratigraphy will once again be needed to help us correlate our wells, understand connectivity, and sweep and steer future drilling safely and successfully.

I would like to see much more training in these areas, and also in how the skills and knowledge are applied to exploring for oil and gas, and in successfully developing our resources. It should be a fundamental part of all master's programs. There should also be increased focus and investment in biostratigraphic research programs. How do we deliver a viable, healthy, and sustainable future? I would argue that we need more bespoke programs — these may be dedicated entirely to biostratigraphy (as offered by the University of Birmingham, UK) or be themes as part of existing master's courses. We must also proactively seek out research programs and begin to recreate the domain expertise in universities as well as in industry. By addressing these areas we might be able to keep this area of applied geoscience alive and take it off its current 'life support' status. The challenge is ours — this skill area is core, and in many cases critical, to safe operations and sound business decision-making.

References

Bailey, H and R Jones (2012). Threat of extinction. *Geoscientist* **22** (4), 6.

Palaeontology is science for everyone!

David A Eberth

Palaeontology brings the past to life, providing perspectives on who we are and where we come from — the original *ancestry.com*! More than any other science, palaeontology is great storytelling, where incredible narrative arcs describe the parade of ancient life across a vast four-dimensional canvas of space and time. We relate to these stories because fossils — no matter how bizarre they may appear — were once like us: actors enlivening the shared stage of the earth.

Dinosaurs are palaeontological icons and an endless source of fascination. At their most awe-inspiring they are monstrous yet safely extinct (except for birds, of course), and it takes little effort to incite interest in them. New forms with tongue-twisting or tongue-in-cheek names (*Masiakasaurus knopfleri* is an example of both) are announced to great fanfare, and newly discovered aspects of their lives (how they looked, moved, breathed, ate, pooped, reproduced, grew, or otherwise interacted with their world) garner significant attention almost daily in the scientific and popular media.

And while it is sometimes tempting to wonder if the hubbub surrounding palaeontology and dinosaurs leaves much room for real science, look closely and you can see the scientific method carefully at work. Colourful stories are grounded in documentable evidence, and observations and hypotheses are wrung through the machinery of theory constructed at the intersections of geology, biology, and physics. As such, palaeontological conclusions and hypotheses are testable with new discoveries, and are readily accessible to other science practitioners.

As demonstrated by the science-and-showmanship of Waterhouse Hawkins, Barnum Brown, Roy Chapman Andrews, and most recently, Stephen Jay Gould, the dual roles of palaeontology as science and entertainment have been inexorably intertwined for more than 200 years. Palaeontological professionals and museums are keenly aware of these dual roles and the expectations they impose. Special palaeontological discoveries remain carefully guarded secrets that are rolled out only in conjunction with extensive media coverage. Emerging technologies, such as 3D scanning, are eagerly pressed into service to reconstruct dinosaurs and their environments in breathtaking new ways. Newly unveiled exhibits, web sites, and a stream of social media chatter constantly refresh our notions of the past, while providing ample opportunity to share reactions and

More than any other science, palaeontology is great storytelling,
where incredible narrative arcs describe the parade of ancient life.

opinions. And palaeontologists are routinely called upon to anchor documentaries, weigh in on various hypotheses, write books and articles, and lecture to appreciative audiences.

Occasionally, the science–entertainment machinery breaks down, allowing speculation and pet theory to supersede verifiable science. But like all science, palaeontology is self-correcting. And in some cases, a correction may actually result in a story evolving into something even more exciting. Witness the revelation that *Archaeoraptor liaoningensis* — a supposed bird–dinosaur intermediate concocted from fossil bits by an enterprising Chinese peasant in the late 1990s — was actually a composite of two new and distinctive Cretaceous fossils: the bird *Yanornis* and a truly bizarre four-winged non-avian dinosaur, *Microraptor*, that glided through the ancient forests of northeast China using large flight feathers on both front and hind limbs. The truth, most definitely, may be stranger than fiction!

Above all else, however, palaeontology is a wonderful means by which children and the public can be introduced to mathematics, engineering, and science in ways that build a comfort with and appreciation for the scientific foundations of modern society. For example, physics, mechanics, and engineering all help explain how sauropod dinosaurs — the largest-known land animals — were constructed and avoided being crushed by their own weight. Evolutionary biology explains skeletal similarities of dinosaurs and allows us to define what a dinosaur is and isn't (hint: they all walked on their toes and had uniquely erect hind limb postures). Mathematics and statistics help predict how many dinosaurs there are still to be discovered (high hundreds to low thousands). And even chemistry, the bane of students worldwide, risks becoming fun when pressed into service to help explain exciting new discoveries of fossilized muscle and blood vessels in 66-million-year-old dinosaurs from Montana.

Palaeontology is a great science because it inspires curiosity about the world, and allows us to share our wonder about the past, present, and future. Palaeontology is science for everyone!

Pollen for people with allergies

Gunn Mangerud

During the spring a lot of people suffer from a pollen allergy. As a result, many don't look forward to this lovely season. Some of us, however, enjoy pollen season all year round — we are palynologists studying, in my case, ancient pollen, spores, and marine plankton. Our pollen samples are locked away in rock as microfossils — the perfect type of pollen for people with allergies: no sneezing, coughing, or watering eyes!

Pollen and spores have an amazingly resistant wall construction, with the result that they are often well preserved in the geological record. The particles are very small, typically becoming part of the silt-sized sediment fraction (<20 μm). We use them to date sedimentary rocks or as proxies for palaeoenvironment or palaeoclimate, since we know that plants (and plankton) are sensitive to climate.

The word pollen is derived from Latin and means flour or dust, an apt name. Pollen and spores are exchanged during the plant reproduction cycle, and plants rely on wind or other transport mechanisms for dispersal. They are distributed in enormous numbers. For people suffering from allergies, pollen distributed by wind is very troublesome but for geologists it is extremely useful. Its tendency to be carried long distances means that we find pollen far away from the areas where it was produced. For example, pollen from hinterland species can be found in offshore ocean basins.

Palynologists use a standard procedure to remove all the rock surrounding these microfossils by applying acids in a series of treatments to concentrate a sample of organic residue. When placed on a microscope slide, the pollen and spores in this residue can then be analysed by counting and recording the numbers of each pollen and spore species present. The points in geological time where we see the first occurrence and subsequent extinction of some marker species can help us identify the rock sample's age in millions of years. This information can be extremely useful for producing correlations in time between rock outcrops and buried sequences of rock that can only be accessed by drilling expensive wells.

During the Late Triassic in the Barents Sea, an enormous delta built out filling in the vast basin that existed in this area. There are no tall plants growing in the

Arctic today but, due to continental drift, this area was then situated further south in a warmer climatic zone, around 45 degrees north, and rich vegetation covered the surrounding land. As the basin filled, pollen and spores were deposited in large numbers along with the sedimentary particles that form the bulk of the rock.

~10 μm

Left: Bisaccate pollen *Protodiploxypinus minor* with two sacci can be carried long distances by the wind. Right: Monolete spore *Leschikisporis aduncus* produced by ferns growing on a Triassic delta in the Barents Sea.

A typical feature observed in outcrop and well samples from the Early Carnian, some 200 to 235 million years ago, is a monolete (elongate scar) spore called *Leschikisporis* which is recorded in particularly high abundance. The spores are produced by ferns and they are found together with another spore produced by a tree-like plant, lycopsid, that typically grew along rivers or in more humid areas. Due to their relatively large and dense form, spores like these were not transported very far, thereby providing information on the type of plants that grew nearby when the sediments were being deposited. As a result we know these trees and ferns must have dominated a vast delta plain that extended relatively far out into the basin.

However, above this interval, later in the Carnian, we see a change. There is more bisaccate pollen (pollen with two sacci). These pollen are similar to those produced from present-day conifers; the two sacci enables them to be transported long distances by wind and they tend to become more common relative to spores the further you are from the shoreline. This change implies that relative sea level rose and the delta plain flooded, pushing the shoreline landward. The appearance of marine plankton in the same samples supports this. So despite the fact that the sediments were deposited in a marine setting, the pollen and spores that they contain can tell us a story about the palaeovegetation on the surrounding shores — a story written millions of years ago, and read only now by palynologists.

Quantitative palaeontology

Benjamin J Sloan

For a few hundred years palaeontology was largely an exercise in properly identifying and classifying fossil remains. Up until the 1980s, scientists relied on hand drawings, written descriptions, and the occasional photograph to assist them with their palaeontological investigations. Classifying fossils and interpreting the nature of the strata in which they were discovered were qualitative tasks; the tools of the trade included shovels, brushes, sieves, microscopes, and notebooks. Quantitative information was tabulated manually on paper.

With the advent of the computer, quantitative palaeontology emerged on several fronts. With the ability to capture, store, and manipulate digital data related to fossils, we gained the ability to analyse and understand our data, and derive previously obscured relationships. Let's look at how this evolution of the discipline transpired with two examples.

Digital data tables

Before the digital age, micropalaeontologists and biostratigraphers were concerned first with identification, aided by published drawings of specimens, and then with the presence or relative abundance of a species in a sample for purposes of understanding stratigraphic age or environment of deposition. Diagnostic 'marker species' were especially interesting as they were considered critical for placing rocks within a stratigraphic age or formation. Published studies frequently included data tables reporting the absolute or relative abundance of species by sample location and/or depth in a well. Many studies were of a limited scope with regard to geography or stratigraphy and did not summarize results over larger areas.

Efforts in the 1980s led to the capture of count data digitally where it was stored in tables on personal computers. Additionally, published data tables of interest to researchers were digitized and stored. With the ability to store and analyse millions of samples representing the full fossil assemblage from all corners of the globe and all stratigraphic ages, a new quantitative biostratigraphy emerged. Scientists adapted probabilistic methods (such as cluster analysis and principle components analysis) from other disciplines and applied them to large quantities of microfossil data to discern subtle trends. Fully numeric comparisons of

With the ability to capture, store, and manipulate digital data related to fossils, we gained the ability to analyse and understand our data, and derive previously obscured relationships.

large sample sets, each sample with dozens of different microfossils, could be made and similarity indices calculated to establish co-occurrence of species, measure diversity, or identify subtle biostratigraphic breaks and unconformities. Modern methods have extended to automated identification of microfossils using image analysis tools (see also *Biostratigraphy at a distance*).

Macrofossil imagery

At the other end of the size spectrum, vertebrate palaeontologists have evolved from digging up and making plaster casts of dinosaur bones to digital imaging of fossils in situ and after recovery. Scientists use LiDAR laser scanning to map bone sets and create high-resolution 3D models of specimens. Non-invasive x-ray computer tomography, adapted from the medical and forensic world, has been applied to digitally explore the interior of fossil remains, revealing structures important to understanding their genealogy, function, and evolution. The computerized representation of fossils in 3D allows them to be effectively animated for further study, understanding, and even entertainment. Widely accessible 3D models of type specimens provide efficient means for obscure fossil fragments to be identified and conclusively tied to their full remains.

Fossil identification is just the beginning. Large publicly accessible databases of fossil specimens of all ages and locations, containing digital morphological information, can be cross-checked with databases on environmental conditions to reveal new patterns of ecological significance. New insights into animal behaviour and evolution seem certain.

QUANTITATIVE · METHODS · CULTURE

Rework your interpretations

Morten Smelror

Many years ago, when the exploration of the Barents Sea was in its early stages, I was examining microfossils in shallow cores taken from the western margin of the shelf. I was particular interested in organic-walled microplankton found in the core samples. They are only a few tens of microns (1/1000 mm) in size, but there were thousands of them.

Microfossils are very useful when you work with small samples, such as pieces of core. Organic-walled microfossils are resistant to degradation, and are often present when calcareous microfossils are dissolved by chemical processes in the sediments. Among the organic-walled microfossils, dinoflagellate cysts are often superior to other fossils because they were usually short-lived in geological terms. Most dinoflagellate taxa underwent relatively rapid evolutionary changes, resulting in a diversity of species characteristic for short periods of the earth's history. Because of this, they are good biostratigraphic markers, and are very valuable tools for dating marine sedimentary rocks.

Looking through the microscope lenses my eyes swept over numerous specimens with beautiful names like *Areosphaeridium diktyoplokum, Dracodinium varielongitudum, Eatonicysta ursulae*, and so on. My job was to find the age of the cored sediments. And I soon found an answer: an age somewhere around Early to Middle Eocene — 48 to 50 million years old. Sample after sample appeared to contain more or less the same assemblage of microfossils. Except for the last one: the sample from the deepest part of the core, and therefore the oldest according to basic principles of stratigraphy. Here I found a few younger Pliocene or Pleistocene species. I thought this was most likely contamination from the laboratory when the sample was processed. No, I was quite sure. Forty samples with Early to Middle Eocene species, one sample with some Pliocene–Pleistocene stuff. I made my report.

A few days later I got a call from the project manager. Prepare for a shock, he told me. Datings based on isotopes of argon from layers of volcanic ash in the core gave an age of 2.4 million years. The few Pliocene–Pleistocene specimens were the ones that were actually in situ. The thousands of Eocene specimens were in fact reworked into the much younger sediments.

Most dinoflagellate taxa underwent

relatively rapid evolutionary changes…

Because of this, they are good biostratigraphic markers.

Today we have a better understanding of the geological history of the western Barents Shelf. During the past three million years the shelf has been subjected to several phases of uplift and erosion. During several major and minor glaciations, large quantities of sediments have been eroded from the shelf in the east and north, transported westwards by the ice and water, and then dumped in huge fans along the shelf edge in the west. In the most active periods of erosion, the amount of sediment transported from east to west was equal to 50 000 dump trucks per day! If you carefully study cores from the huge depositional fans along the western margin, you can actually detect a reversed stratigraphy. The older parts of the fans contain the sediments eroded first, and as the younger glaciations dug deeper into the sedimentary succession on the shelf, an increasing proportion of older and older fossils were reworked into the succession.

There are lessons to be learned from this story:

1. Never for a moment believe that you have the full story covered. Geology, palaeontology, and biostratigraphy are combinations of observations and interpretations. Even the most careful observations will only give small and erratic pieces of what was originally there.

2. Put maximum effort into careful observations. When there is nothing left that has escaped your eyes, the best possible interpretations will automatically follow.

3. Check and re-check the sample-processing workflows. Are samples properly handled, are they switched, or have they been contaminated? (In my library I have a wonderful paper written by a Chinese palaeontologist in which he described how he mistakenly described a fragment of burned candlewick as a Precambrian microfossil!)

4. Do not always trust the geochronologist … they may have been caught out by contaminated samples or erroneous measurements.

5. Remember the famous words of Galadriel in *Lord of the Rings*: 'Even the smallest creature can change the course of the future.'

Signed up for the duration

Simon Payne

Fresh-faced from university I joined one of the UK's biggest biostratigraphic consultancies as a foraminiferologist in the early 1980s. The North Sea industry had long outgrown short trousers but was still relatively youthful, new plays such as the Eocene were yet to be discovered and drilling west of Shetland seemed wildly optimistic. Biostratigraphy was largely an exploration tool, and the analysis of individual wells, their aggregation into sub-regional studies, and sporadic wellsite work were the stock-in-trade for a thriving organization. The company was geared up to produce a standard product with little room for manoeuvre, an effective way to channel the labours of a lively, young population into a consistent and repeatable format.

At the time, few of the mid-sized or smaller client oil companies employed in-house biostratigraphers. It sometimes seemed that our potentially critical input was viewed with a scepticism that could border on the unhealthy. Our entirely valid use of Latin names hardly rendering our contribution more intelligible. Biostratigraphy could quite readily be bulldozed out of the way by the client oil company if it failed to support their subsurface model. While seismic data could be re-processed at a cost of millions of dollars, biostratigraphy — less expensive by at least two orders of magnitude — was a one-shot wonder. It was often undertaken with little background data, sometimes even without wireline logs. Biostratigraphy seemed to sit at arm's length from the main event.

It wasn't just about money. Seismic processing might take a matter of months to complete but our Achilles heel was the time taken to produce a full bios-tratigraphic report for a well. At the other end of the spectrum, so-called hot shot samples could be dropped on us from the North Sea by helicopter with little or no notice and a head-spinning turnaround time to be met. Visits to oil company offices met with a varied, occasionally bemused, reception. A query as to how we could credit a microfossil with the specific name of *trivialis* did little to engender a feeling that we were batting for the same team. Or indeed that we were on the same planet.

I recall a field trip to the Scottish highlands in my early days where we intro-duced ourselves around the table on the first evening. On informing everyone that I was a micropalaeontologist I was roundly informed by a voluble geophysicist with a well-drained glass, 'A micropalaeontologist? You deserve all the shit you get!' This took me back a couple of years to when I held a summer job, tasked with trying to impose biostratigraphic data, hitherto unsullied by use, onto the well stock of a major North Sea operator. One day I was told of an impending visit by the in-house biostratigraphers, a group ordinarily safely corralled overseas, and was asked to hold the fort. An impressive array of bigwigs turned up to shrug and harrumph in splendid isolation, most of the geoscientists having tactically taken the day off. I perceived uncomfortably that biostratigraphy was all well and good when it agreed with seismic and geological models, but could be discarded when it suggested something different, an important piece of the jigsaw puzzle left under the sofa without demur.

Thinking back to university days and my indulgence in matters soft rock and palaeontological, the number of students in palaeontology classes beyond first year had seemed quite low. Perhaps having to draw bivalves on a Friday afternoon left a taint that followed people into industry. Could this Victorian microfossil circus have an impact on a multimillion dollar well? The unwritten rule seemed to be that the older and harder the rocks, the more kudos was attached. However, while Early Palaeozoic Dalradian amphibolites might tell a remarkable story — whisper it — forams and calcareous nannofossils are remarkably effective in understanding the petroleum geology of the Neogene in so many global basins.

In those days it felt to me as though biostratigraphy and petroleum geology were a bit disconnected — part of the same family but distant cousins — and both were diminished as a result.

Specialists are special

Simon Payne

I started my career at a large consulting company (see *Signed up for the duration*). After the alarums and excursions of the mid-1980s oil-price crash I found myself on the other side of the fence in a large oil company as part of an extensive biostratigraphic group. Ways of conducting business had been gradually changing, with less analytical microscope work retained in-house and more shared among selected consultants. This was a sign of greater trust between client oil companies and consulting firms (whence a growing number of us had sprung), a greatly increased workload, and the realization that exclusivity was seldom justifiable on technical or financial grounds.

Biostratigraphers were housed alongside the preparation laboratories and our sedimentological kinfolk. 'The zoo', as it was termed, sat semi-detached from the business world upstairs and teemed with scientific kit and a cast of interesting characters. A visit to the laboratories was a treat for geologists and geophysicists wanting to understand more about this specialized underworld. They might even meet the injured guillemot, smuggled in for (an ultimately successful!) recuperation.

Any walls that might have existed between the individual biostratigraphic sub-disciplines were being torn down, despite the occasional retrograde comment. Isolated pockets still persisted in the view that, 'We are the cavalry, the geologists are the foot-soldiers', which seemed to me both disingenuous and misguided. However, this was a confident group — science was king and we felt bullish about our role in the geo-firmament.

Changes were afoot that further boosted the profile of biostratigraphy, pulling it closer to the mainstream. Sequence stratigraphy bounded onto the scene with the force of the space-hopper craze of my childhood — soon every exploration geologist worth his salt was scrawling LST, TST, and HST onto wireline logs, while geophysicists mapped offlaps, onlaps, and downlaps. The gurus were ushered in to preach to the eager congregation, ripe for conversion. Because sequence stratigraphy is all about chronological correlation, biostratigraphy became everyone's friend, and now we sat alongside geologists and geophysicists in integrated teams. Momentum gathered to such an extent that 'specialists are special' became the mantra, with biostratigraphy amply recognized for its contribution in well correlation, palaeonvironmental determination, and seismic calibration. Discipline networks arose to ensure greater sharing of methods and practices.

But nothing could shelter us from the real world of languishing oil prices that persisted through the 1990s and biostratigraphers suffered a series of mass extinctions along with our mainstream colleagues. For those who remained, work practices changed disconcertingly, as our microscopes were wheeled away. As environmental stress shapes adaption and evolution, we started to change in response. We morphed, with varying degrees of discomfort, into 'biostratigraphic coordinators' and 'informed buyers', although being a micropalaeontologist without a microscope felt at first like being a cavalryman without a horse.

As the North Sea and West of Shetlands matured, a tranche of Palaeocene reservoirs became ripe for development from the mid-1990s onwards and we received every encouragement from management, geoscientists, and engineers to join the collective effort. The cry from field-development geologists that 'the biostratigraphy has all been done' was swept away as broad exploration-scale biozonations were superseded by finer-scale bioevents that could help to characterize reservoir time-slices and sub-environments more effectively.

The consultancies were an essential element in this new world. Some older, perhaps more conservative, empires were fragmenting and vigorous new ones were springing up like mammals in the Palaeogene, seeking to occupy new niches through innovation. Field-specific biozonations were being developed and their efficacy tested to help monitor and control the drilling of development wells on the rig. The willingness of consultants to carry embryonic ideas to wellsite gave them an increasingly influential voice in operational decisions.

Gone was the straitjacket of validation against a regional or global biozonation; our focus had changed to a brutal geo-pragmatism. 'Anything goes' was writ large as abundance trends, assemblages, absences, reworking — indeed any scraps of biostratigraphic data — were tested for their potential as a field-scale bioevent. Experimentation in the quest for geological application was the order of the day. This further emboldened biostratigraphers in the exploration and appraisal realm, as confidence in refining stratigraphic resolution was passed back along the food chain. 'More bang for your bug' was with us; biostratigraphy itself was merrily evolving.

Over the past decade and a half these substantial tweaks to the sphere of biostratigraphy have become firmly embedded and the discipline has moved along once again. One day — when the pace of things slows just a little — I will write the next installment of this story.

Stand up and make some noise!

Sissel Kvernes

As a student doing a thesis in biostratigraphy I was the designated nerd of the geology community — quite an achievement! On joining the oil industry as a fresh reservoir geologist I met a lot of old goblins saying, 'Oh, biostratigraphy — we don't do that. It doesn't work... just a waste of time and money'. Not the most receptive start I could have had.

When I joined the biostratigraphy specialist team, I discovered yet another breed of geologists. These were easier to work with, but I soon realized that they were just saying thank you and ticking the biostratigraphy box without really applying it to their projects. My data just disappeared into a database black hole.

Luckily another type of geologist did exist. These wanted help applying the data to their models. 'Can we sit down for a day then you can explain what this means?' they would ask. The more questions asked, the more this group became comfortable with their biostratigraphic data — and the more involved they got. References to biostratigraphy popped up in reports and presentations. I was starting to see that how I was received as a biostratigrapher was based on one thing: their experience and knowledge of the topic.

I'm now back as a reservoir geologist after over six years as a specialist biostratigrapher, and talking with my new colleagues I have found the same situation as before — they don't know how to use biostratigraphic data. I think the reason for this is lack of training, both in universities and the oil industry, on how to properly use the data. Most people know how to put the data into software, but there is a total absence of discussion about how to use it when creating a geological concept. The result is that geologists seem reluctant to use biostratigraphic data to its full potential, so the datasets just sit there occasionally appearing in correlation panels. It's rare to hear someone ask, 'Does this have any implications for our geological model?'.

When I started in my new job as a reservoir geologist the department had just begun a project on structural geology. After a few weeks they came to me saying, 'We might need some timing and stuff... can you help?' And so I was recruited into a project consisting of two structural geologists, two geophysicists, ... and now a biostratigrapher. And to make a long story very short, within the next

I was starting to see that how I was received as a
biostratigrapher was based on one thing:
their experience and knowledge of the topic.

year we changed the geological concept dramatically, went against the current model in the company, and annoyed several people.

Before I came into the project they already had a lot of ideas for a new concept. Adding the biostratigraphy data was the piece of the puzzle that enabled them to believe in their ideas, and create new ones. It created a framework for what was possible. The biostratigraphy alone does not provide a solution — all the pieces of the puzzle have to fit — but it is just as important as the seismic data and the logs.

The biggest challenge I had in the project was to break down the biostratigraphic data into something the rest of the group could work with. I have always joked, 'The best way to scare a geologist is to throw Latin at him'. And I have seen biostratigraphers do exactly that, presenting lists and lists of fossils, and within 30 seconds you can see the curtains going down. The biostratigraphic community have to take some of the credit for any ill disposition that geologists have towards them. After a few weeks with my fellow project members, I realized that simplification was key, so I started with a few erosion surfaces and biostratigraphic events. After playing around with the data and making small sketches of how the results related to the geology, the ball started rolling and jaws dropped. People said, 'I had never seen the point before, but this really works'. Structural geologists and hardcore geophysicists were starting to get their heads around what biostratigraphic data could do for them.

Working in reservoir geology suddenly made me very visible as a biostratigrapher. It also showed me that if we are to take geological understanding to the next level, then biostratigraphy has to be used properly. You will not necessarily win popularity contests — there are still a lot of geologists out there in love with their models. What is important is to get your specialists out in the business. Don't lock them away from the great people at the sharp end of the organization.

Biostratigraphers: Never mind where you sit or what they say to you; stand up and start making some noise!

Systematic collection
Jens Lehmann

Growing up in a fossiliferous area in Westphalia, north Germany, I have been digging for fossils for most of my life. There were many outcrops in the vicinity of our home and I got rich practical experience of where to find which fossils. It's a truism, especially in palaeontology, that you need to be patient to be successful. Some fossils are rare and only a systematic approach will uncover them. Early on I started to collect in a scientific way, progressing bed-by-bed and documenting what I did. However, although already an experienced collector, I did not experience how randomly fossils can be scattered in the individual geological units before starting my PhD.

My fieldwork in the Late Cretaceous of Lengerich and Brochterbeck, Westphalia, included archaeological-style methods, systematically unearthing several square metres of finely bedded marlstones, an elementary method in antiquarian studies that is still little used in modern palaeontology. However, the most astounding observation I made was based on an even more primitive method. My work area included mainly limestone–marlstone couplets that were deposited on the ground of an epicontinental sea, way off the former coastline, and probably related to Milankovitch cyclicity (e.g. Gale et al. 1999). Single beds appear completely uniform within the outcrop, with no beds pinching out or showing any irregularities in facies and lithology. This lithologically boring

Collecting fossils in monotonous limestone–marlstone couplets of the Late Cretaceous, north Germany.

succession with mostly unattractive fossils — often poorly preserved as internal mould — was never systematically collected bed-by-bed. But simply hammering off as much material as possible for each single bed revealed staggering results. (Of course, one needs permission and restraint for this sort of collecting.)

One part of the story is that extensive collecting did reveal a remarkably rich fauna with many new species for the region and for the strata; for example, the first belemnites — usually very rare in this stage in Germany. A more prominent result, at least from my point of view, was the dispersal of fossils. It was notably heterogeneous, most fossils did not occur singly but in clusters. Some clusters contained fossils of the same groups (e.g. only echinoderms or brachiopods), some represented a mixture of different invertebrates. The nature of associations was obvious for only a couple of clusters: body chambers of ammonites were a shelter for organisms randomly washed in — a phenomenon described in many other strata and known as sheltered preservation (e.g. Maeda & Seilacher 1996). The majority of clusters were accumulated either by bottom current (the mixed invertebrates), probably in small depressions on the sea floor, or represented small benthic *in vivo* associations (the monospecific assemblages).

What does this tells us?

1. Even the most uniform and lithologically homogenous strata are not uniform in their fossil content. One could argue that my example focuses on a shelf environment that underwent dynamic processes, but it is true even for deep-sea sediments that are believed to be very stable. Deep-sea cores of various international drilling programs often reveal finds of whale bones or shark teeth even though these represent a minute amount of material from each single bed.

2. The quality of basic field data is key for the understanding of palaeoenvironments. Even as a 'computer palaeontologist' — a term used by Dolf Seilacher to tease students — high-quality palaeontological data are the result of hands-on business. It needs a lot of rock-smashing and concretion busting — simple and exhausting but academically useful — for some basic results, with the welcome side-effect of clearing your mind.

References

Gale, A S, J Young, N Shackleton, S Crowhurst, and D Wray (1999). Orbital tuning of Cenomanian marly chalk successions: Towards a Milankovitch time-scale for the Late Cretaceous. *Philosophical Transactions: Mathematical, Physical and Engineering Sciences* **357**, 1815–1829.

Maeda, H and A Seilacher (1996). Ammonoid taphonomy. In: Landman NH, K Tanabe, R Davis (eds) Ammonoid Paleobiology. *Topics in Geobiology*. Plenum Press, New York. 543–578.

Thank your mentors

Catherine Burgess & Craig Harvey

With the general reduction in the number of biostratigraphy graduates over the last decade (Bailey & Jones 2012) and the ever-increasing importance of stratigraphy (and other specialist geoscience subjects) in unravelling earth history for business purposes, such as exploration for hydrocarbons, we wanted to reflect on our respective but independent journeys into biostratigraphy.

We both began with a child's enthusiasm for fossils, after all how many pre-schoolers don't love dinosaurs? In our case neither of us quite grew out of it, amassing collections of 'maybe fossils' from walks along the beaches in southern England or the Jurassic Cotswold Hills. An interest in the physical sciences through school led us to select geography and geology and both of us were fortunate to have teachers who were hugely passionate about geology and that engaged, encouraged, and expanded our interests in and beyond school.

We diverged in our university degree choices, one selecting natural sciences at Cambridge University with an aim of specializing in astrophysics, with interest in geology being outweighed, at that time, by enthusiasm for the night sky. The other steered towards pure geology at Anglia Ruskin University with a hope that it would lead to a job in the great outdoors. At university, the first year for both of us comprised impenetrable subjects such as crystallography, but also our first real fieldwork in the Lake District and the Alps — a revelation. Rocks really do fold; there is the outcrop to prove it! Suddenly geology became tangible; you could explain what you could see around you. Fieldwork really helped build a sense of community and that helped in making later choices, such as specializing in geology rather than astrophysics! In the remaining undergraduate years at our respective universities, we deepened our interests in sedimentary geology and palaeontology and with the support of influential and enthusiastic supervisors, colleagues, and more fieldwork, we became attracted to microfossils, quantitative data, and biostratigraphy concepts.

This grounding helped us make the choice to pursue higher degrees in biostratigraphy, one taking the direct approach with palynology at Sheffield, and the other a more roundabout route via palaeoclimate at Cardiff University. The authors ultimately met over a poster during Palaeontology 2007, where we discussed that it was more than OK to be a specialist, that jobs do exist in

We have found it rewarding to be as open, constructive,
and flexible as possible on our journey as you
never know in what direction you may go.

industry, and that having a solid geological foundation such as biostratigraphy at your core will hold you in good stead. For both of us further study felt like a natural step, thanks to those people who had inspired and supported our curiosity over the years. One of those supporters was Francis Witts, a Harvey family friend, who gave me (Craig) the chance to undertake PhD fieldwork in Venezuela when all other avenues failed. I funded myself by working part-time until I got a scholarship from Sheffield University. Francis also alerted me to an antique book sale in Bath at which Anglia Ruskin was selling all the old books from the geology department which had closed. We bought a load, keeping some and donating the rest to Sheffield palynology department where I was studying at the time. Francis showed me to think beyond myself and connect to the bigger picture or a higher purpose.

One tremendous characteristic that appears common among the people that have influenced us is their ability to communicate a subject simply and passionately enough for listeners to 'get the concept', which provides a basis from which to further deepen one's understanding. Overall, we have found it rewarding to be as open, constructive, and flexible as possible on our journey as you never know in what direction you may go, neither of us expected our early interest in fossils to take us where it has. Indeed, we may have wandered a bit but because of influential people we were never lost. For this we would like to say a profound thank you to all of those who took time to encourage us — you were role models and we aspire to be the same.

One final thought, for those of you that recognize similar influential people in your life, have you told them the positive impact they have had on you? If not please go and tell them; it will make their day.

References

Bailey, H and R Jones (2012). Threat of extinction. *Geoscientist* **22** (4), 6.

The fossil guardians

Bodil Wesenberg Lauridsen

The sound of the helicopter is earsplitting and the rotor wind is so strong that the only thing you can do is crouch over the luggage and try to prevent it from flying away. Away like the helicopter. Once it has left the silence is overwhelming. I look at my field partner. Now it is only her, the sedimentologist, and me, the palaeontologist, for the next five weeks, alone in the wilderness of northern Greenland, the first two women ever to set up a camp here. We have a hammer and a .44 Magnum each, and a rifle to share.

We are here to give colour to one of the few grey spots remaining on the geological map of the world. A few hours later two orange tents, a radio mast, and a trip-wire alarm warning against polar bears change the scenery. The colourful tents make us feel better in the vast expanse of grey rock, plants, ice, and water. Even the few birds are grey. The white polar bears keep out of sight. On the radio, base camp wishes us goodnight.

* * *

The outcrops in the riverbanks are our main targets. Only a few metres high but tilted continuously so kilometres of stratigraphy can be logged based on the profiles. A convincing boundary marks our starting point. Sandstone, storm sandbeds, siderite horizons, conglomerates — the sedimentologist is happy. She is sharpening her pencil and drawing logs. I look desperately at all the sand. Where has all the ancient life gone?

She continues with minute precision. My eyes scan the ground. I know the shapes I am looking for, but all I find are trace fossils. No body fossils. Lunch is a welcoming break, but soon it feels better to work and keep warm. There is snow

My eyes scan the ground. I know the shapes
I am looking for, but all I find are trace fossils.

in the air. The only convincing fossil shapes I identify are in the snow-filled clouds. We work till late in the 24 hours of daylight. Life feels less complicated when we are tucked into our sleeping bags.

And then it is as if a little fairy hears my wishes. One day the ground is scattered with siderite nodules full of inoceramids. No one was expecting them but here they are, popping right out of the ground. I keep on smiling and soon the sedimentologist is also convinced that these beautifully preserved bivalves are all you can wish for, if you want to date Late Cretaceous sediments.

Bivalves are normally not very useful for biostratigraphy due to their low preservation potential, adaptive morphology, and local distributions. However, the inoceramids are extremely valuable for stratigraphic purposes with their easily fossilized calcitic valves, rapid evolutionary changes, and wide geographical distribution in a variety of facies. In the Late Cretaceous they display a speciation rate of 0.2 to 0.5 species per Ma. Back home in the tent, the literature provides me with names of all our finds. So many new stories can be told. These sediments are some of the important pieces missing in the Mesozoic puzzle of the Arctic. Having identified the zonal markers, the age of each interval we're logging can be identified. Calibration and correlation to other outcrops is now possible and we can start colouring in the last areas on the geological map with sedimentological and stratigraphical certainty. This is big news for understanding the geology of the Arctic. That night we deserve dessert.

Days go on and the sample bags get filled. We collect, draw, discuss, take pictures, and fill the diaries with field notes. For every ammonite we find, we collect ten inoceramids. Our only breaks are when the snowstorms rage and we are forced to stay in our sleeping bags for long days.

Then one day we spy a female polar bear with two small cubs. For minutes we look at one another, then we fire warning shots and they decide to take off. They will guard the fossils until next time we come. It is, after all, their country.

We are being evacuated now.

The lure of fossils

Bert Boekschoten

Fossils are remnants from the past, and museums are for keeping things for the future. In fossil museums, we have a double guarantee for durability! Of course fossils predate museums which have existed only since the 17th century. Their heyday came in the 19th century, fueled by national pride in exploration and curiosity about natural history.

In their founding phase, temple-like museums stored tangible evidence for scientific reliability. Material was accumulated from avid amateur collectors — such as schoolteachers and clergymen, adding to their income — working on temporarily exposed fossiliferous deposits along the many new railway lines. Curators had a relatively large staff of (mostly self-taught) technicians. The first excavations of fossils for their own sake took place.

Next came a consolidation phase. Excavations became more refined and curators more specialized and less accessible. In the 1950s, exhibits commonly still sported their carefully transcribed Indian ink notices written more than 50 years before, as exhibitions certainly were not the first priority of conservators. Indeed, curators were mainly interested in producing monographs and less concerned with unsorted and puzzling materials, not realizing that such content can make museums the best place to hunt for significant new discoveries.

Unsurprisingly, public attendance waned. I remember a Scandinavian museum with excellent collections, but the display cases could not be opened, even for study purposes. So we hung around for three days in the lofty and well-lit — but sadly visitorless — premises. This invasion caused quite a stir; upon learning we were Dutch the administration put up 'No cigar smoking' signs everywhere supposing every Hollander was an inveterate smoker (we were not). And a beautiful north Italian fossil museum, which I thought I had to myself. I enjoyed its timeless atmosphere and did not notice an overweight guard asleep on a bench in the shade of a fossil palm tree. My shuffling around awoke her with a wild shriek that rattled my nerves, and the bones of a giant aquatic turtle, but had no other effects in this mortuary.

A third phase of museum practice now took over as public financial support sagged, and the number of paying visitors became paramount. Presentation was

CURATION · METHODS · CAREERS

To this day, education remains a museum's cash cow.
The visitor participates in the evolutionary stampede from
Proterozoic Gunflint algae to Neanderthal humans.

professionalized, lighting and display emphasized, and functional anatomy and ecology were new issues. The scant visitors of old would necessarily bring in their own interests and stories, but the numerous new public largely consisted of schoolchildren and lay people that needed packaged themes and expected interactive displays. To this day, education remains a museum's cash cow. Instead of the static systematic subdivision of fossil material, the visitor participates in the evolutionary stampede from Proterozoic Gunflint algae to Neanderthal humans. Incomplete local collections are augmented with casts of key specimens, incomplete imaginations with lurid video presentations.

My mentor, the venerated Professor von Koenigswald, was a leading mammal palaeontologist and considered fossils, shells, and teeth to be elegant mementos from a remote past. So he gave not a second glance to bones; such things were for doctors treating victims of alpine sports. Skulls, though, fascinated him — he surrounded himself with Tyrolean skulls decorated with red roses and blue gentians — and his deep dedication to the beauty of palaeontological specimens was genuine and enticing. He loved to tell the public tall stories about his specimens and the science of palaeontology.

I love small museums animated by dedicated enthusiasts. A small, communal, museum in a tiny German village comes to mind. Patiently, a single family of fossil gatherers collected material over the course of many years from a quarry in their municipality. Their (mostly unspectacular) finds were thoroughly studied by serious researchers and are now on view in the village hall. Information is offered in unrelenting scientific jargon to the tourist that drops in on a rainy day. And yet: this works! People leave impressed by the family's dedication and inspired by the involvement of the palaeontologists, expressing themselves in their clumsy professional lingo.

Such small museums are sadly vulnerable to neglect and closure. Meanwhile larger fossil museums may change beyond recognition. What remains is the lure of the fossils themselves. Let's sort out these remains with curiosity, and cherish these wonders as the crown jewels of our science.

The megaspore big show: discovery

Peter H Morris

It seemed that there was little left to discover after 25 years working as a micro-palaeontologist on the Mesozoic succession of the northwest European shelf. Routine well analysis had become predictable, with the biostratigraphic evalua-tion divided on a discipline basis: non-marine, Triassic–Jurassic formations were invariably off-limits to micropalaeontologists… until 2006. With the drill-ing of Statoil's 6608/11-4 exploration well, I was thrust into the world of an alien group of microfossils: megaspores.

Well 6608/11-4 is located in the Haltenbanken area of the mid-Norwegian shelf, just to the north of the Norne and Urd fields. Both fields produce oil and gas from Early and Middle Jurassic reservoirs. The main objective of 6608/11-4 was to evaluate similar aged formations, including the non-marine Åre Formation. It was probably through sheer desperation that the biostratigraphic program conceived for this well led to the continuous micropalaeontological analysis of ditch cuttings and core samples down to TD (total depth). Normally paly-nological analysis would have been applied, however previously this had been disappointing because preparations were invariably dominated by morphologic-ally diverse, long-ranging miospores.

When the first megaspores (up to 1 mm in diameter and visible to the naked eye) started to appear in my sample residues, my initial feelings were of curios-ity and wonder. Later, as the deeper samples yielded greater numbers, trepida-tion set in — how was I to speciate and start logging these alien microfossils? Despite the crudeness of my attempts at speciation, two important conclusions could be initially drawn from the well data. Firstly, megaspores could be readily extracted in large numbers using conventional micropalaeontological prepara-tion methods. Secondly, a distinct succession of megaspore assemblages was evident within the Åre Formation — the potential for biozonation was starting to emerge.

Statoil's biostratigraphers could see that megaspores had potential, and I became involved in a sequel well — 6608/11-5 — and then a multi-well study of the Urd Field. By this time my library of megaspore publications was growing, with the consequence that the systematics of the Åre Formation megaspores had improved. In addition, I had developed reflected light, colour photomicroscopy of megaspores using a Bresser ocular digital camera, which in combination with Helicon Focus imaging software, enabled several focal-plane images to be combined into one.

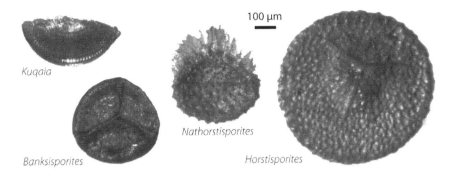

100 µm

Kuqaia

Banksisporites

Nathorstisporites

Horstisporites

With more confidence, a detailed megaspore biozonation of the unit was proposed. The succession of megaspore assemblages seen in the Åre Formation appeared correlatable with those in the Danish Basin and beyond; there also seemed to be a link between the change in megaspore-producing floras and climate through the Late Triassic and Early Jurassic. All this was presented in an internal report, which was about to be assessed independently by the leading academic in the fields of palynofacies and megaspores.

My first meeting with Professor David Batten was another milestone in the unfolding world of megaspores. The feelings of a viva exam initially prevailed in David's cramped office, piled ceiling-high with palynological publications. His critique of my work was generous, and I was directed to publications hitherto unknown to me. On seeing a photomicrograph of one of the more enigmatic zonal species, David leapt to his feet and exclaimed, 'I have seen that before'. He produced a Chinese publication by Cui et al., and the mesofossil *Kuqaia quadrata* was duly identified. Since our meeting in Manchester the advancement of Jurassic megaspore biostratigraphy has been a shared interest, and later we found ourselves drawn to the Middle Jurassic plant beds of North Yorkshire.

The megaspore big show continues on pages 108–109.

References

Cui W, G Zeng, H Zhu, and W Li (2004). Early Jurassic megaspores and palynomorphs from the Bohu Depression, Yanqi Basin, Xinjiang, NW China. *Acta Micropalaeontologica Sinica* **21**, 292–308. (In Chinese, with English summary.)

The megaspore big show: application

Peter H Morris

Even before my meeting with Professor David Batten (see previous chapter), the word 'megaspore' had reached the ears of the Gullfaks Field team within Statoil, who were about to start a major re-evaluation of the Statfjord Formation reservoir model. The hypothesis that the megaspore biozonation defined in mid-Norway had regional application was about to be tested through a pilot study 580 km further south.

It was late on a Friday afternoon when I identified the first megaspores from a key Gullfaks well. After that the growing excitement had to be reined in before I made the phone call to Statoil. What followed, through the spring and summer of 2007, I now recall as a blur of sample crates arriving, rounds of sample processing, picking, and analysis, all to meet impossible deadlines. During the subsequent three phases of work, with assistance from Jake Jacovides, a total of 1600 samples were analysed from 55 wells. An effective biozonal framework was established, enabling the Gullfaks team to make major advances in reservoir modelling. It was a landmark event — megaspores had come of age in the world of applied biostratigraphy.

Other fields producing from the Statfjord Formation have since come under scrutiny, including Snorre, Oseberg, and more recently Johan Sverdrup. In all these fields the original megaspore biozonation scheme has been applied and refined, with new marker species identified. The scope of megaspore research was also extended northwards into the Barents Sea. Here pilot studies not only proved up the regional biozonation, but showed that in this basin, lycopsid megaspore-producing plants thrived at an earlier time in the Late Triassic. Lycopsids are simple, low-lying plants which house two types of sporangia producing either megaspores or microspores. The evidence was building that lycopsid floras continued to evolve through the Triassic and Jurassic, dispersing between basins and regions. But how and why did lycopsids thrive so long beyond their alleged zenith in the Carboniferous, and what were the common factors controlling their distribution and dispersal?

Regional work on the Åre Formation demonstrated that in successive biozones, megaspore acme events are associated with coal and rootlet beds, characteristic of delta-top, peat-mire facies. It was also evident that the Rhaetian–Hettangian shift in climate was critical, with the development of wet and humid conditions favouring lycopsid floras. But humidity was not the only factor determining megaspore generation because the host plants required a colonizing platform — the delta top and associated environs. In the Jurassic of the Eurasian region, deltaic development mostly ties in to sea level low-stands, the Early Hettangian being a case in point. The study of megaspores in the Barents Sea showed that these conditions prevailed at an earlier time in the Late Triassic. Here a distinctly different megaspore microflora had evolved, with new zonal species.

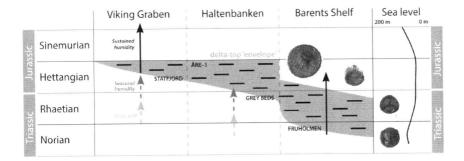

Regional data demonstrated that lycopsid floral distribution closely followed delta-top facies through space and time; in effect this plant group colonized and evolved within an envelope that met the optimum conditions. Megaspore count data showed that once this envelope was established megaspore production was massive: over 1500 per 100 g of sediment. From the delta top, megaspores were then dispersed throughout the upper and lower delta-plain channel systems, along with millions of their microspore counterparts (often lumped with *Deltoidospora* miospores).

The 'megaspore big show' was repeated again in the Middle Jurassic, when due to thermal uplift localized fluvial-deltaic systems prograded simultaneously south into the Cleveland Basin and north into the Viking Graben. Yet again a changeover of lycopsid floras is evident from the new megaspore species appearing. This pattern appears to have continued into the Early Cretaceous of the Weald Basin: after that, along with other ancient plant groups, the lycopsids went into decline — the era of the angiosperms had begun.

Further reading

Morris, P H, A Cullum, M Pearce, and D Batten (2009). Megaspore assemblages from the Åre Formation (Rhaetian–Pliensbachian) offshore, mid-Norway, and their value as field and regional stratigraphic markers. *Journal of Micropalaeontology*, **28** (2), 161–181.

The submerged forest at Borth

Denis Bates

The submerged forest at Borth, Wales, is one of those rare geological features that allows us to connect with the geological past because of its spectacular nature and immediacy. My own interest in the forest dates back to the 1960s when the remains of an auroch (an extinct bovine) were found there. The discovery — by the local butcher of all people — resulted in a number of members of the university congregating on the beach to recover the skeleton from the foreshore. Since then periodic visits to view the 4500-year-old preserved forest have resulted in a series of observations made over the years.

The forest itself has been known since the early 20th century (and probably before; Ashton 1920) and among the earliest workers at the site was Harry Godwin from Cambridge who produced the first pollen diagram from samples taken through the peats (Godwin & Newton 1938). Since then researchers have examined the forest applying dendrochronology to the trees (Heyworth 1985), while others have examined foraminifera and ostracods (Adams & Haynes 1965, Haynes et al. 1977), and the sediments themselves (Shi & Lamb 1991). The most recent research has been undertaken by archaeologists from the University of Wales Trinity Saint David who began work in 2011.

The construction of a new coastal defence system accidentally resulted in the stripping of sand covering the peat close to the cliffs at the south end of the beach. I was on one of my periodic visits to the forest and noticed oddly shaped fragments of beach pebbles in the peat. A phone call to my son (a geoarchaeologist) in Lampeter resulted in the discovery that these stones were in fact remnants of burnt beach pebbles discarded in the forest after some unknown use. Following a visit by the Lampeter team, further discoveries included preserved animal and human footprints in the proximity of the site. Since then, the storms of early 2014 enabled large transects of the forest to be examined and records made of the features preserved beneath the beach. Consequently we now realize that, rather than a continuous expanse of forest, the environment at the time was one of wet woodlands dissected by a major channel filled with very different sediments to those traditionally associated with the forest. This channel now appears to be the probable source of the auroch remains and may well have been a focus of human activity within the landscape.

We anticipate more discoveries. At the time of writing further investigations are on-going, in association with additional sea-defence works. However, the work at the site is not just about scientific discovery. It's also about the human dimension of the forest and what it means in terms of climate change and the area around Borth, both in the past and today. The construction of the new coastal defences are a present-day response to exactly the same pressures felt by past populations when the forest was being inundated by marine waters perhaps 4500 years ago. Borth has been here before.

The loss of the forest also has a resonance with the local legend of Cantre'r Gwaelod, the lost kingdom of Cardigan Bay. Here, as in so many of our coastal landscapes, stories abound of lost kingdoms beneath the sea so it seems fitting to leave Borth with the lines of the poem *Clychau Cantre'r Gwaelod* by J J Williams (1869–1954), translated by Dyfed Lloyd Evans:

> *Beneath the wave-swept ocean / Are many pretty towns*
> *That hearkened to the bell-rings / Set pealing through the night*
> *Through negligent abandon / By a watcher on the wall*
> *The bells of Cantre'r Gwaelod / Submerged beneath the wave*

References

Adams, T D and J Haynes (1965). Foraminifera in Holocene marsh cycles at Borth (Wales). *Palaeontology* **8**, 27-38.

Ashton, W (1920). *The evolution of a coast-line*. Edward Stanford Ltd, London.

Godwin, H and L Newton (1938). The submerged forest at Borth and Ynyslas, Cardiganshire. *New Phytology* **37**, 333-344.

Haynes, J R, R Kiteley, R Whatley, and P Wilks (1977). Microfaunas, microfloras and the environmental stratigraphy of the Late Glacial and Holocene in Cardigan Bay. *Geological Journal* **12**, 129-159.

Heyworth, A (1985). *Submerged forests: a dendrochronological and palynological investigation*. Unpublished PhD thesis, University of Wales.

Shi, Z and H Lamb (1991). Post-glacial sedimentary evolution of a microtidal estuary, Dyfi Estuary, west Wales, UK. *Sedimentary Geology* **73**, 227-246.

Thinking outside of the burrow

Duncan McIlroy

Right from its earliest days as a modern scientific discipline, ichnology — the study of trace fossils — has bridged the gap between sedimentology and palaeontology. As ichnologists we don't generally have any clear idea of what made the burrows that are left in ancient sediments and bedding planes. The beauty of the discipline is in determining what the fossils can tell us — 'sleuthing' as one of my students dubbed it. To be a good ichnologist requires a broad knowledge base, of course, and plenty of imagination. And because it is an immature science, there is still a bewildering amount to see and do and learn.

Trace-makers are generally animals, so we need some biological background, particularly:

- **Biodiversity** — what kids of animals are there out there that might have made the trace fossil we are studying?

- **Biomechanics** — what are those creatures capable of doing and how do they do it?

- **Functional morphology** — how does an organism gain the necessities for life such as food and shelter?

Often the critical pieces of information that biology might provide for the ichnologist, 'What type of burrow does an animal make?' and 'What does the animal do in its burrow?', are unknowns. Biologists might at best know the shape of the open burrow an animal makes, but seldom do they consider the changes to the position of the burrow through the life of the animal. This opens up the important but underexplored discipline of 'experimental neoichnology' — the study of living trace-makers. There are few things that make this ichnologist happier than to be able to directly observe an animal in its burrow.

Even the most enthusiastic ichnologist will admit that the most important clues when interpreting a rock succession with trace fossils in it are actually sedimentological. Early in my career, my biggest shortcoming as an ichnologist was a poor knowledge of sedimentological processes. Only by understanding sedimentological context, is it possible to determine whether a trace fossil or assemblage of trace fossils is out of place. That kind of integrated sediment-ological–ichnological approach to palaeoenvironmental ichnology had its

There are few things that make this ichnologist happier than to be able to directly observe an animal in its burrow.

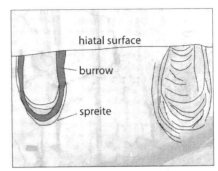

The trace fossil *Diplocraterion* partially eroded by cross-bedded sandstones (Ordovician of Australia).

greatest proponent in Roland Goldring. He devised the ichnofabric approach to ichnology which forces the user to take account of the sedimentological context of trace fossils. During my PhD, Roland was always harassing me to cut up my trace fossils. It was only after I had taken a 10-year hiatus from being a dedicated ichnologist to focus on sedimentology, sequence stratigraphy, and petroleum geology that I really began to appreciate ichnology. Now I cut up trace fossils all the time.

This might seem extreme. The collecting, classifying, and care of beautiful fossils is something all palaeontologists love. To cut fossils up and destroy them still seems like a sin to the pure palaeontologist in me, but it yields so much insight. By relying on crack-out and bedding plane trace fossils, ichnologists often missed out on what the trace maker was actually doing. My current research focuses on three-dimensional digital reconstruction of trace fossils and their ichnofabric, employing serial grinding and photography, combined with petrography, geochemistry, and the measurement of porosity and permeability.

The future of ichnology is in understanding burrows in the context of the near-burrow environment, both ancient and modern. That those animal–sediment interactions also change the reservoir properties of hydrocarbon reservoirs is a bonus that makes our discipline increasingly relevant in the real world. If the next generation of ichnologists is to advance the science, we need biologists, sedimentologists, and palaeontologists capable of thinking outside the burrow.

Topsy-turvy bird phylogeny
Alan Feduccia

Palaeontology was forever changed with the 1996 unveiling of the small Chinese Cretaceous dinosaur *Sinosauropteryx*, sporting a mane of thick filaments along its back. With only a small black and white photo, the *New York Times* proclaimed that the structures were some sort of proto-feathers and somehow supported the theory that birds were dinosaur derivatives. The discovery was the apparent culmination of a palaeontological revolution that started in the late 1960s when Yale's John Ostrom discovered the birdlike dromaeosaur *Deinonychus*, reviving the hypothesis that birds evolved from dinosaurs. The hypothesis implied that flight must have originated from the ground up. The view for most of the 20th century was that birds originated from small tree-dwelling archosaurs (antecedents of dinosaurs) that developed flight by the more logical route taken by all other airborne vertebrates — parachuting and gliding, from the trees down.

The next shock came just two years later when the editor of *Nature* triumphantly announced 'the debate is over'. The cover story featured two putative dinosaurs, *Protarchaeopteryx* and *Caudipteryx*, with true avian pennaceous flight feathers on the wing. These discoveries codified birds as living dinosaurs, and established this mantra as the keystone discovery of modern palaeontology. Yet, these discoveries were not properly vetted and lacked normal scientific stringency. The field abandoned the normal scientific falsification approach in favour of simply working to confirm what was already thought to be known. Quickly a consensus was achieved, and all disbelievers of the orthodoxy were banished.

Before long, fantastical proposals — ranging from diverse hot-blooded dinosaurs sporting proto-feathers, to dinosaurs with bird wings for insect traps — began to emerge. Junk science prevailed, propelling the fanatical creationists to dub the phenomenon the 'Disneyfication of dinosaurs'. To many of us who have long endured the often rancorous debate, however, this scheme is far afield from the reality of avian evolution, a topsy-turvy phylogeny that has no reality in fact. Just what is in error in the newly devised scheme?

The figure (from Feduccia 2012, modified from a diagram adapted from *National Geographic*) shows a popular version of what has become the most accepted phylogeny of birds. It shows the progression from avian ancestor to modern birds.

From left to right is the small 'feathered dinosaur' *Sinosauropteryx*, followed by the Late Cretaceous birdlike *Velociraptor* (thought to be close to avian ancestry), followed by the two *Nature* caudipterids (*Caudipteryx*, second, with true avian wing feathers), and only then followed by the Jurassic iconic urvogel *Archaeopteryx*, an early Cretaceous bird *Eoalulavis*, and finally the modern crow. Regrettably, this avian family tree is in total error, a chaotic arrangement!

Let's reconsider the evidence. *Sinosauropteryx*, with its greatly reduced forelimbs, has nothing to do with avian ancestry and the 'proto-feathers' have been shown to be nothing more than collagen fibres supporting a lizard-like frill. The Late Cretaceous *Velociraptor* of *Jurassic Park* fame is very birdlike, and may well be among the assemblage of avian derivatives that reverted to a terrestrial existence. The caudipterids, with reduced but true avian flight feathers, are in reality secondarily flightless birds — they evolved from flying ancestors but were no longer capable of flight — with myriad birdlike features remaining; they are in a sense Mesozoic kiwis. Then there is *Archaeopteryx*, truly close to the ancestry of birds, and in many aspects a bird in the modern sense. It is followed by an opposite bird (enantiornithine) — named 'opposite' because of its reversed shoulder bones — representing the dominant land birds of the Mesozoic; and finally the modern crow.

My view, now shared by many, is that the Chinese fossils bearing modern feathers are indeed early birds, some having acquired secondary flightlessness. This view may seem revolutionary but it hearkens back to the predominant view of the 20th century. Namely that flight originated by the intuitively and biophysically facile trees-down model, in tree-dwelling basal archosaurs, with feathers originating in the context of jumping, parachuting, and gliding. This scenario is in stark contrast to birdlike dinosaurs sprouting feathers and all their sophisticated avian flight architecture in a non-flight context, so-called exaptations. Such a topsy-turvy scheme is practically non-Darwinian. The tried and true axiom still holds: if it has feathers and avian wings, it's a bird!

References

Feduccia, A (2012). *Riddle of the Feathered Dragons*. Yale University Press, New Haven.

Ackerman, J (1998). Dinosaurs take wing: The Origin of Birds. *National Geographic*, **July**, 74–99.

What is an ammonite?

Christian Klug

First, we should clear up some confusion: the term 'ammonite' applies only to most Mesozoic forms. By contrast, ammonoids — a subclass which contains the ammonites — originated over 400 million years ago in the Early Devonian and vanished along with most dinosaurs after 335 million years of existence. So the question should really be, 'What is an ammonoid?'.

Simply put, ammonoids are relatives of squid, but without the ink sacs. They had a shell with gas-filled chambers which enabled them to float and swim efficiently with little effort. While ammonoids do not appear in the fossil record until the Early Devonian, the evolutionary lineage that lead to them can be traced back via the bactritids to the orthocerids — a highly successful group of cephalopods with straight conical shells. They had dome-shaped chambers connected by a tube called the siphuncle through their centres. The shape of septa changed as the cross section and coiling of the shell was modified through evolution. Firstly, the shell cross section changed from circular to oval, causing the suture lines (where the septum is attached to the shell wall) to become slightly vaulted. Secondly, the siphuncle slowly changed from a central to a ventral position, thus giving rise to the group we call the Bactritida. The Bactritida are poorly known, but phylogenetically important, because they gave rise to all living squid, octopuses, and the extinct ammonoids. Thirdly, how did an ammonoid evolve from a bactritid? The change was possibly driven by the dorsoventral asymmetry with the shifted siphuncle — some bactritids began

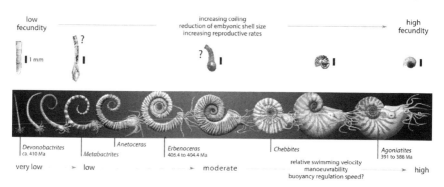

Evolutionary changes around the transition from Bactritida to Ammonoidea including (top to bottom) fecundity, embryonic shell, adult shell shape, and other attributes.

building slightly coiled shells. That's when some conjecture comes in, because the classification of ammonoid is given when the shell forms at least one whorl. This is a bit arbitrary, but at least it's a definition.

A whole series of evolutionary changes occurred around the origin of ammonoids. Many of these changes are linked with increased coiling. Perhaps most importantly, the aperture moved more and more upward with tighter coiling of the shell, to a point where the aperture wound up slightly higher than the centre of mass of the animal. This enabled the animal to swim reasonably fast, much faster than their bactritid ancestors. The increase in horizontal swimming speed was of utmost importance; it helped the ammonoids catch prey and evade the increasingly mobile forms of jawed fish, which evolved in the Late Silurian and Early Devonian; some of them were certainly hunting cephalopods. Possibly, the selective pressure of the increase in mobility of predatory fish accelerated the evolution of more tightly coiled shells and thus the embryonic shell became smaller, from around 1 cm to about 1 mm in diameter. Simultaneously, the adult body chamber volume increased from circa 10 to 10 000 cm³. Presuming that the reproductive organs changed in the same proportion, we can estimate that the number of eggs produced by one female rose from approximately 200 in an early ammonoid to 200 000 in Late Devonian forms. This high number is comparable to reproductive rates of some modern pelagic squid, underlining similarities in their ecology and evolutionary origin. The small size of eggs and hatchlings appears to explain their susceptibility to environmental change. Accordingly, they became nearly extinct several times, but they also diversified rapidly, perhaps due to their swimming abilities. Finally, the increase in coiling (with eventual whorl overlap), the reduction of embryonic shell size, and the increase in the number of septa (chamber walls) until adulthood, caused the septa to become much more complexly folded.

And why are ammonoids so important today? In contrast to the pearly Nautilus, ammonoids had a greater number but much smaller eggs. Thus, the small hatchlings were more sensitive to ecological changes. As a result, entire clades of ammonoids vanished and were replaced rapidly by others. These spread quickly over vast regions, making them the icon of index fossils.

What is homeomorphy?

Rosemary Titterton

I first contemplated homeomorphy in an exam hall, answering a question set by John Haynes for the end of year master's exams at the University of Aberystwyth. The question was something along the lines of, 'Compare and contrast the alveolines and the fusulines'. Simple. Both are foraminifera but the fusulines are calcareous and Carboniferous and the alveolines are porcellaneous and Cenozoic. But of course the question went deeper than that.

Why? Both lineages have larger forms that are fusiform in shape, but one was from the Carboniferous and the other from the Cenozoic. Why should, or even could, nature repeat itself in two such distinct groups? And why do larger forms want to get so large? What are the mechanics that allow a single-celled animal to become so large and cigar shaped that you can imagine picking it up and smoking it?

Closer examination reveals the differences in the ontogeny of the families. Fusulines have secondary septae which divide the chambers. They have no aperture on the last chamber but an apertural face with septal pores. In alveolines the initial proloculum is followed by a spiral passage that becomes planispirally coiled. Secondary septae are formed parallel to the direction of coiling and the test walls are imperforate. Apertures are round pores in the apertural face corresponding to the position of the chamberlets.

But these are details. My favourite paper explaining homeomorphy in the planktonic foraminifera is Neagu (2005). He observed that two similar environmental events — intervals of global maximum sea temperatures — correspond to two principal times of evolutionary radiation in planktonic foraminifera. First the Late Albian rotaliporids and hedbergellids at the time of maximum sea levels at the Albian–Cenomanian boundary. Then a second period of maximum temperature in the Coniacian which resulted in explosive radiation of the marginotruncanids and rugoglobigerinids. Neagu concluded that the same causes lead to the same results during the evolution of certain groups: 'Owing to similar environmental changes… the organisms react also alike'.

Caron (1985) described examples of homeomorphy in her clear and precise

Why should, or even could, nature repeat itself in two such distinct groups?

summary of the Cretaceous planktonic foraminifera which many of us refer to constantly. She explained: 'The interaction of form and function forces the tests of the Globigerinacea to develop morphological characters that reoccur several times during the Cretaceous in members of different lineages'. Her taxonomic overview helps the biostratigrapher recognize this convergence of form and illustrates several examples.

Another example of homeomorphy was described by Keen (1988) in his detailed review of the cytherettid ostracods. He suggests that the Tethys Ocean was a barrier to migration and restricted their distribution to the northern hemisphere, mostly Europe, until the Late Palaeogene. Species occurring in South America, South Africa, and southeast Asia assigned to the family are homeomorphic and not true cytherettids. He also warned us that within the family the development of a tricostate exterior ornament has occurred independently several times.

So beware when you have to invoke reworking or caving to explain the juxtaposition of the fossils you see. Reflect a little on the possibility of homeomorphy and look a little closer if the preservation allows it — and the strength of your microscope, the steadiness of your hand, and most of all your patience. Detailed analysis by the taxonomists may reveal different lineages; but usually the industrial (or industrious) micropalaeontologist doesn't have the time.

For the non-micropalaeontologists who wonder why we sometimes change a species name and subsequently the age and correlation, homeomorphy may be the explanation. Only the fossils are perfect.

References

Caron, M (1985). Cretaceous planktonic foraminifera, in Bolli, H, J Saunders, and K Perch-Nielsen (eds.). *Plankton Stratigraphy*. Cambridge University Press, Cambridge. 17–86.

Glaessner, M F (1972). *Principles of Micropalaeontology*. Hafner Publishing Company, New York. 297 p.

Keen, M C (1988). The evolution and distribution of Cytherettid Ostracods. In: N Ikeya, K Ishizaki, and T Hanai eds. *Evolutionary Biology of Ostracoda: Its Fundamentals and Applications*. Elsevier Science. 967–986.

Neagu, T (2005). Albian Foraminifera of the Romanian Plain. *Acta Palaeontologica* **5**, 311–332.

Why do we have all this stuff anyway?

B Strilisky & J Gardner

Palaeontological collections don't exist because people love looking at old bones or because salaried hoarders called curators or professors feel the urge to save every fossil they come across during their careers. Collections serve myriad purposes, including:

- Long-term preservation of historically, culturally, or scientifically important objects.
- Supporting academic research.
- Educating and inspiring the general public.

All laudable endeavours, but do these benefits warrant the often substantial costs of building and maintaining palaeontological collections? It may seem hard to justify all those cabinets and shelves filled with, for example, multiple examples of eerily similar-looking hadrosaur vertebrae. It sometimes looks like every single fossil was picked up indiscriminately and stashed away to be forgotten, like in the famous warehouse scene at the end of *Raiders of the Lost Ark*. Whenever budgets are tightened, you see high-level bureaucrats skeptically peering through warehouse doors and asking, 'Why do we have all this stuff anyway?'

Let's start off by recognizing that, first, palaeontology is the study of ancient life and, second, fossils are the only direct evidence for ancient life. It thus follows that archiving fossils and their associated information is essential to ensure their safekeeping and accessibility for both the present and the future, and to facilitate advancements in the field. For various historical and practical reasons, museums and universities have proven to be the best (although admittedly not perfect) venue for maintaining such collections.

Fossils are cool, but we don't need to collect every one we come across. That's neither the best use of our finite resources nor is it responsible. At least some of the time, effort and expense invested in collecting, cataloguing, conserving, and storing our new hadrosaur vertebrae could probably have been spent in other equally responsible ways: for example by conserving the ones that were collected 20 years ago before they deteriorate past the point of repair. The collecting that occurs is (or should be) done systematically and purposefully, but there will always be exceptions. Sometimes an opportunity arises that is too good to pass up; e.g. a coveted specimen comes onto the market or we have a once-in-a-lifetime chance to collect at a remote locality. Other times, museums are compelled to accommodate unplanned acquisitions such as donations from private collectors, objects they are mandated by law or administrative decree to accept, or orphaned collections that deserve to be saved. With so many potential avenues for objects to come into a collection, it's no surprise that the storage cabinets fill up over the decades.

It's easy for most people to appreciate why a museum would gladly house several flashy dinosaur skeletons in its inventory, but to return to our example of hadrosaur vertebrae, why would we want to keep so many examples of those kinds of fossils? (As of October 2014, the Royal Tyrrell Museum of Palaeontology has about 150,000 specimens and 588 isolated hadrosaur vertebrae in its collections.) There are at least two overlapping reasons why that happens. The first has to do with variation. Unlike manufactured items, such as cars, for which every model produced in the same year is essentially identical, individuals of a biological species are inherently variable. This variation occurs even within one localized population at a single point in time; think, for example, of differences within your community between females and males, among individuals of different ages, and even among individuals of similar ages. Throw in variation that occurs among populations in different places and at different times, not to mention variations induced by injuries, disease, and other life events, and it is easy to see why multiple examples of a species are needed to provide at least a snapshot of the potential variation within each species.

The second reason has to do with the vast amount of time and geography represented in the fossil record and the large number of species that have lived in the past. For example, how many millions of animal and plant species must have lived on Earth during the 180 million years of the Mesozoic Era? Even if a collection is geographically and temporally focused (e.g. the Late Cretaceous of Alberta), documenting the taxonomic diversity from even that restricted region and interval with adequate fossil samples is going to take up a lot of storage space.

If we are concerned about the sizes of our current palaeontological collections, perhaps we should be thankful that the fossil record is so geographically, temporally, and taxonomically patchy and that it samples only a fraction of the entire history of life on our planet!

List of contributors

Haydon Bailey has a PhD in chalk micropalaeontology, is a chartered geologist, and has worked as a consultant micropalaeontologist in the oil and gas industry for more than 35 years. He still specializes in Upper Cretaceous chalk stratigraphy, although work has led to projects throughout much of the geological time scale around Europe, Africa, and the Middle East. He is currently President of the Geologists' Association. Since 2012 he has been Honorary Lecturer on the master's course in applied and petroleum micropalaeontology at the University of Birmingham.

Never ignore the bits you don't recognize   *78*

Denis Bates graduated from Queen's University Belfast and gained his PhD there in 1965 on the Lower Palaeozoic rocks of Anglesey, North Wales. He was on the staff of the University College of Wales (now Aberystwyth University) for 40 years, from 1960–2000. He has worked on a number of Palaeozoic fossil groups: brachiopods, trilobites, crinoids, and particularly graptolites. And he is still working on them!

Golden graptolites   *60*
The submerged forest at Borth   *110*

Martin Bates graduated in archaeology from the University of London and completed a PhD in Quaternary dating frameworks for river terraces in Northern France. He now lectures in geoarchaeology at the University of Wales Trinity Saint David campus in Lampeter. He is working on Pleistocene and Holocene deposits from Orkney to Jersey, and is particularly interested in submerged landscapes.

Decoding Quaternary sea levels   *40*

Bert Boekschoten studied palaeontology at Utrecht University, Netherlands, with G H R von Koenigswald, and graduated there in 1968 with C W Drooger. He began his career as a staff member, later professor in palaeontology, at Groningen University with P H Kuenen, and moved to Amsterdam VU University in 1985. There he remains active as a widely travelled palaeontological naturalist. He is a Waterschoot van der Gracht medalist, and an avid fan of Wagner operas.

The lure of fossils   *104*

Andrew R Bowman is a graduate of Syracuse University and the University of North Carolina–Chapel Hill. He completed his PhD from the University of Nebraska (Lincoln) in 2011, with a focus on calcareous nannofossil biostratigraphy of the Palaeogene. He began his career as an industry biostratigrapher with Unocal in 2003, and later worked for Chevron from 2005–08. In 2008 he joined Statoil, where he is currently a biostratigrapher primarily involved in deepwater Gulf of Mexico.

Lentic jeff and other bugs   *72*

Mike Bowman retired from BP in 2011 and has since taken up a part-time chair in development and production geology at the University of Manchester. In 2012 he was the President of the Petroleum Exploration Society of Great Britain. At his retirement he was BP's functional and Global Head of Geoscience. In addition to his role at Manchester, Mike is a non-executive Director for Enegi Oil; he also advises and consults for independent oil and service companies and gives courses and lectures on geology and the oil industry.

Our core skill 82

Martin Brasier is the Professor of Palaeobiology and a Fellow of St Edmund Hall, Oxford University, UK. Other duties have included serving as Chairman of the Faculty of Earth Sciences; Dean of Degrees at St Edmund Hall; Chairman of the Subcommission on Cambrian Stratigraphy; membership of NSF panels; and membership of NASA panels on life on Mars. In 2014, he was awarded the Lyell Medal for his work on the context of events leading up to the Cambrian Explosion. Martin holds a professorship at Memorial University, Newfoundland, Canada, and is the author of several books including his textbook on microfossils as well as *Secret Chambers* and *Darwin's Lost World*. His hobbies include playing jazz piano.

Nothing is sacred 80

Catherine Burgess holds a BA and MSci in natural sciences from the University of Cambridge and a PhD in palaeoceanography and palaeoclimatology from the University of Cardiff where her research was focussed on the Middle Eocene of New Zealand. She has worked for Shell for five years and is currently a stratigrapher with Sarawak Shell Berhad in Miri, Malaysia.

Thank your mentors 100

Simon Conway Morris holds a Chair in Evolutionary Palaeobiology at the University of Cambridge, where he is also a Fellow of St John's College. He graduated from the University of Bristol, and worked under the supervision of Harry Whittington for his PhD. He is well-known for his work on the Burgess Shale and the Cambrian Explosion, as well as on evolutionary convergence. The former is summarized in *The Crucible of Creation* and the latter in *Life's Solution* and *The Runes of Evolution*. He has won various honours, and was elected to the Royal Society in 1990. When undisturbed he can be found reading G K Chesterton with a glass of wine immediately to hand.

Bioastronomy 30

Alex Cullum is a geologist, palaeontologist, and author currently working within exploration for Statoil in Stavanger, Norway. He studied at Aberystwyth University in Wales and his PhD was on the biostratigraphic correlation of sequences in Arctic Canada. Psychology and how we communicate science and the things that matter are the subject of his latest novel.

Fossil hunting with a six year old 54
Golden graptolites 60

CONTRIBUTORS

Tony Doré is a Senior Advisor at Statoil with a global exploration remit. He was previously VP of exploration North America. Tony has published more than 50 peer-reviewed papers, and edited six books. He has served academia and industry in various capacities, and in 2010 was appointed as an Officer of the Most Excellent Order of the British Empire (OBE) for services to geology. He shares a house in London with his wife and far too many guitars.

Don't lose your plagiosaur

Jason A Dunlop studied zoology at the University of Leeds and palaeontology at the University of Manchester, UK, before taking up his current post as Curator of Arachnids and Myriapods at the Museum für Naturkunde in Berlin, Germany. He primarily works on fossil Arachnida and their significance for understanding the evolution of arachnids and their relatives. He is also Secretary of the International Arachnological Society.

Draw carefully

David A Eberth is a Senior Research Scientist and writer at the Royal Tyrrell Museum of Palaeontology in Drumheller, Alberta, Canada. He specializes in the study of dinosaurian environments, stratigraphy, and fossil preservation. He has published and presented more than 100 scientific papers based on fieldwork around the world. He has also organized numerous symposia and co-edited books and chapters on bonebeds, dinosaurs, and Alberta's geological history. His current interests focus on how advances in the biological and earth sciences impact society and culture.

Palaeontology is science for everyone!

Alan Feduccia's research centers on the origin and early evolution of flight, feathers, and endothermy. He is also interested in the evolution of birds through the Tertiary, the K-Pg extinction event, the origins of flightlessness, embryology, and avian systematics. He is S K Heninger Distinguished Professor Emeritus and former Chair of Biology at the University of North Carolina, Chapel Hill.

Topsy-turvy bird phylogeny

James Gardner is the former Collections Manager and now the Curator of Palaeoherpetology at the Royal Tyrrell Museum of Palaeontology in Alberta, Canada. Jim's research focuses on the evolutionary history of lissamphibians (frogs, salamanders, caecilians, and albanerpetontids), especially those from North America. When not pondering dead amphibians, Jim enjoys gardening, reading, fermented beverages, binge watching TV shows on DVD, and the slower pace of small-town Albertan life.

Why do we have all this stuff anyway?

Felix Gradstein has worked as a micropalaeontologist/stratigrapher and petroleum geologist for Esso Canada in Calgary, the Geological Survey of Canada at the Bedford Institute of Oceanography in Nova Scotia, and Saga Petroleum in Oslo, Norway. As adjunct professor for many years he guided over 20 postgraduate students in stratigraphy and micropalaeontology at Dalhousie University, Canada, and at the University of Oslo, Norway. He has authored or co-authored over 170 scientific publications (including 15 books) including *Geological Time Scale 2012* (Elsevier). From 2000–08, he served as Chair of the International Commission on Stratigraphy (ICS) and in 2008 received the International Gryzbowski Award for dedicated service to the profession and excellence in the field of micropalaeontology, and in 2010 the Jean Baptiste Lamarck Medal from the European Geosciences Union for outstanding achievements in the field of stratigraphy. He is Professor at the Natural History Museum, University of Oslo, Norway, and Visiting Professor at the innovative Micropalaeontology Institute of Unisinos, Sao Leopoldo, Brazil.

Øyvind Hammer has an MSc in mathematical modelling and a PhD in palaeontology from the University of Oslo. He has worked mainly at the Natural History Museum (NHM) in Oslo and at Physics of Geological Processes in Oslo, and is currently Associate Professor at NHM. He has published in several fields including invertebrate palaeontology, water–rock interactions, hydrocarbon seepage, marine geology, stratigraphy, and statistical methodology. His favourite eon is the Phanerozoic.

Craig Harvey holds a BSc in geology from Anglia Ruskin University and an MSc and PhD in palynology from the University of Sheffield where his research was focussed on the Lower and Upper Palaeozoic. He has worked 14 years for Shell, joining Shell UK as a stratigrapher before moving into exploration with subsequent postings in Norway, Saudi Arabia, Qatar, and now Oman. Before joining Shell, Craig worked for Ichron as a palynologist.

Donald Henderson is Curator of Dinosaurs at the Royal Tyrrell Museum of Palaeontology in Drumheller, Alberta, Canada. His main research interests are functional morphology of dinosaurs, plesiosaurs, pterosaurs, and other extinct giants; and anything to do with fossil trackways (dinosaurs, mammals, early tetrapods). He makes extensive use of mathematics and computing in his research in the form of 3D digital models and animations.

Lars van den Hoek Ostende is a researcher at the Naturalis Biodiversity Center, Leiden, Netherlands. A specialist in fossil insectivores and insular faunas, his primary interest lies in the biogeography of the past, or, in short 'what was when where and why?' The first thing you should know about palaeontology, in his opinion, is that cooperation beats competition any day.

Into the mouth of the mouse 70

Jørn H Hurum is a Professor in Vertebrate Palaeontology at the Natural History Museum, University of Oslo. He studied palaeontology at the University of Oslo and completed his master's and a PhD on Late Cretaceous multituberculate mammals. As a post-doc he studied skull morphology in tyrannosaurid theropods. Since 2001 he has worked in Svalbard, on a late Jurassic Lagerstätte, and on early primates when, in 2007, the Natural History Museum acquired the only complete fossil primate ever found, nicknamed Ida. Hurum is a 2011 National Geographic Emerging Explorer.

Fossil hunting on eBay 52

Christian Klug studied geology and palaeontology at the Eberhard Karls-Universität in Tübingen, Germany, and at the Northern Arizona University, USA. He completed both his master's degree and his PhD in Tübingen. Thereafter he has worked for the Staatliches Museum für Naturkunde in Stuttgart, and since 2003 at the University of Zurich, Switzerland. In his research he focuses on the palaeobiology of cephalopods.

What is an ammonite? 116

Dirk Knaust is a sedimentologist working as a Specialist in the research department at Statoil, Norway. After graduating in Germany with a PhD in geology (sedimentology and palaeontology), he has been working in the oil industry with exploration and field development. Dirk has studied various aspects of trace fossils and ichnology, which is documented in about 60 publications in scientific journals and edited volumes. He is co-editor of the book *Trace Fossils as Indicators of Sedimentary Environments* (Elsevier).

A trace fossil primer 16

Trine Krathus-Larsen graduated from the University of Århus, Denmark, in 2000 with a master's in geology (Miocene palynology). Since 2002 she has been working within exploration for Statoil and PGNiG Upstream International. She is currently a senior geologist for VNG Norge, Stavanger, Norway.

Dinosaur rock stars 42

Sissel Kvernes is a geologist and biostratigrapher currently working within production for Statoil in Bergen, Norway. She graduated from the University of Bergen in 1999 with a degree in palaeontology. She has worked as a biostratigraphy specialist in Statoil for six years, with a particular interest in the Jurassic of the Norwegian continental shelf. In 2010–11, Sissel was responsible for biostratigraphy on a Brent Group study project.

Stand up and make some noise!   96

Bodil Wesenberg Lauridsen studied the palaeoecology of macrobenthos while a PhD student and postdoctoral research fellow at the University of Copenhagen, Denmark. She now works on the biostratigraphy of bivalves in the Arctic region as a senior researcher at the Geological Survey of Greenland and Denmark.

The fossil guardians   102

Jens Lehmann is Head of the Geosciences Collection of the Faculty of Geosciences at the University of Bremen, Germany. He graduated from the University of Tübingen in 1994, followed by a PhD on palaeoenvironment and integrated stratigraphy, and a postdoc at the University of California, Davis. He now has a permanent position at the University of Bremen and has established an excellent relationship with the Natural History Museum, London, UK.

Systematic collection   98

Gunn Mangerud is a Professor in Biostratigraphy and is Head of the Department of Earth Sciences at the University of Bergen, Norway. She received her master's degree from NTNU, Trondheim, and her PhD from the University of Bergen. She started her career as a biostratigrapher at IKU, SINTEF in 1988 and moved to Norsk Hydro after five years where she worked in different positions within research, exploration, and the petroleum technology division, and later as a chief geologist. After moving back to academia in 2009, her main interest has been biostratigraphy, with a particular focus on the Carboniferous and Triassic of the Arctic areas.

Pollen for people with allergies   86

Allard W Martinius is a clastic sedimentologist specializing in fluvial and shallow marine sedimentology and stratigraphy, as well as reservoir characterization and fauna–substrate relationships. He has an MSc from Utrecht University and a PhD from Delft University of Technology. He works for Statoil and has mostly been employed in the research centre in Trondheim, Norway, with four years in the technology excellence group (both production and exploration) and five years in extra-heavy oil production in Venezuela and Canada. He is currently leading advisor for sedimentology and stratigraphy in production.

Hardgrounds   62

Octávio Mateus is a Portuguese palaeontologist and Professor at Universidade Nova de Lisboa. He grew up and lives in Lourinhã, a town known for its dinosaurs. He has named several new species and conducted field expeditions to Greenland, Africa, North America, and Asia. He discovered and reported the first dinosaurs from Angola and Bulgaria.

Duncan McIlroy began his research career at Oxford University working on trace fossils across the Precambrian to Cambrian boundary under the supervision of Martin Brasier. At present he is Canada Research Chair in petroleum geoscience and leads a research group at Memorial University of Newfoundland which focuses on applied ichnology. He continues to dabble in the Precambrian–Cambrian palaeobiology and ichnology of Avalonia.

Giles Miller has a PhD in Silurian micropalaeontology from the University of Leicester. For the last 20 years he has worked at the Natural History Museum, London, where he is a Senior Curator in the Earth Science Department responsible mainly for the micropalaeontology collections. He is a regular blogger advocating museum collections *www.nhm.ac.uk/natureplus/blogs/micropalaeo* and is currently Chairman of the Geological Curators' Group. Follow him on Twitter *@cgilesmiller*.

Emily Mitchell has a PhD in palaeoecology from the University of Cambridge, UK, and her previous degrees include an MPhil in mathematics from York University, UK, and an MRes in ecology from St Andrews University, Scotland. Her research uses both statistical and theoretical models to further understand the palaeobiology and palaeoecology of Ediacaran organisms.

Peter H Morris started his career in the oil industry with BP and developed research interests in Triassic–Cretaceous micropalaeontology of Europe and the Middle East. Now an independent consultant he continues to work in these areas as well as applied aspects of megaspore biostratigraphy. He recently undertook an evaluation of the Middle Jurassic deltaic sequence in North Yorkshire.

Simon Payne is a Biostratigraphic Advisor for BP Exploration. He has a degree in geology from Queen Mary College, University of London, and an MSc in micropalaeontology from University College London. He worked for Robertson Research from 1983 to 1987 and joined BP in 1988. He has worked predominantly in the North Sea, Egypt, and Angola, and his prime area of interest is reservoir-scale biostratigraphy.

S George Pemberton received his PhD from McMaster University in 1979. He is currently a Distinguished University Professor and the C R Stelck Chair in petroleum geology in the Department of Earth and Atmospheric Sciences at the University of Alberta, Canada. The main thrust of his research pertains to the application of ichnology to petroleum exploration and exploitation. His work has been recognized by a number of awards. He was elected a Fellow of the Royal Society of Canada in 2001; Canada Research Chair 2002–09 in Petroleum Geology; and honorary membership in CSPG in 2010. In 2013 he was the recipient of the Logan Medal from the Geological Association of Canada. He has won 15 best-paper or best-presentation awards, has published over 225 papers, and edited or co-edited seven books.

Imogen Poole worked for over 20 years at various universities across Europe focusing on fossils, predominantly wood, and their role in palaeoenvironmental and palaeoclimatological reconstructions. She briefly held the Chair of Palaeobotany at Oslo University before returning to the Netherlands and undertaking freelance consultancy in modern, archaeological, and fossil wood identification. She now lives and works in Scotland.

Iain Prince Earned his PhD from the University of Wales, UK, studying the palynology of chalks from southern England. He then worked as a biostratigrapher for Geochem Group, RPS, and Statoil working mostly in Norway, Denmark, West of Shetlands, the North Sea, Venezuela, and Angola. In 2008 he joined Shell and he is now head of Shell's skill pool for biostratigraphers around the world.

Mike Romano graduated from the University of Liverpool with a PhD on the Ordovician rocks of eastern Ireland, with an emphasis on the trilobite faunas. He then went on to lecture in the geology department at Sheffield University. This was followed by research into the Ordovician rocks and trilobite faunas of Portugal where he became interested in invertebrate trace fossils. It was then a natural transition into work on the dinosaur tracks of the Middle Jurassic of Yorkshire. He retired as senior lecturer in 2006, but still retains an active interest in tracking Yorkshire dinosaurs.

Enrico Savazzi holds a PhD from Uppsala University and has been a palaeontologist at German, Italian, Japanese, Swedish, and US institutions for about two decades. For several years he has been a technical writer in the IT and telecommunications industry, but continues to publish in palaeontology as a hobby, especially on extreme adaptations, puzzling evolutionary histories, and other subjects that catch his curiosity.

Mike Simmons is the Technology Fellow for Geosciences at Haliburton with a responsibility to investigate innovation in geoscience as applied to the exploration process. Previously he was Earth Model Director at Neftex, and before that worked at BP, Aberdeen University, and CASP. His main interests are applied stratigraphy and the geology of the Tethyan region.

Age is an interpretation 26

Benjamin J Sloan is a geologist and foraminiferal micropalaeontologist. He studied biostratigraphy with modern ecologist Bill Walton at Northwestern University and quantitative biostratigrapher Martin Lagoe at University of Texas at Austin. He has been working at Chevron nearly 20 years and currently manages a deep-water oil field in Brazil.

Quantitative palaeontology 88

Morten Smelror is a geologist, palaeontologist, and the Director of the Geological Survey of Norway. After graduating from the University of Oslo in 1985 he has held several research and management positions at SINTEF and the Norwegian University of Science and Techonolgy. In 2000 he joined the Geological Survey of Norway and in 2006 he was appointed Director General of the Survey. Morten is a board member of the International Scientific Continental Drilling Progam (ICDP), and has been on the editorial boards of several international geoscientific journals.

Rework your interpretations 90

Brandon Strilisky is the Head of Collections Management at the Royal Tyrrell Museum of Palaeontology in Drumheller, Alberta, Canada. He is responsible for the care of more than 150 000 specimens that date from the Cambrian to the Quaternary. Originally from Ontario, Brandon has been in Alberta for almost a decade since completing his master's in museum studies at Newcastle University, UK.

Why do we have all this stuff anyway? 120

Rosemary Titterton has a BSc geology and an MSc and PhD in micropalaeontology studying the recent ostracods of the Solomon Islands. At Robertson Research she worked primarily on the microfaunas of the North Sea. After 16 years as a consultant she moved to Statoil, Stavanger; the first two years as a biostratigrapher and then as a regional exploration geologist with the world as her playground.

What is homeomorphy? 118

John de Vos completed his PhD in biology at the State University of Utrecht, the Netherlands, on the topic of the endemic Pleistocene deer of Crete. He began his career as Curator of the fossil macro-mammals and the Dubois Collection at the Naturalis Biodiversity Center, Leiden, and from 1980 onwards was Curator of the palaeontological and mineralogical cabinet of Teylers Museum, Haarlem, both in the Netherlands. His research interests are: evolution of the genus *Homo* in east and southeast Asia, migrations, dispersals and diasporas in prehistoric island faunas, and fauna development during the Pleistocene in Eurasia. He retired in 2012.

Julia Webb is a Senior Lecturer in biosciences at the University of Gloucestershire in Cheltenham, UK. She stumbled into the forensic discipline in 2004 when she was asked to assist the investigation team examining evidence from a murder in Birmingham, UK. Since then she has worked on more than 50 high-profile cases, mainly in the UK.

Robert W Williams studied physics and geology at Stephen F Austin State University in Nacogdoches, Texas. At SFASU, Williams worked as an instructor in physics and astronomy labs for undergraduate students and taught at the university observatory. From 1980–85, Williams studied geology and astronomy in Norway at the University of Oslo. He received a Candidatus scientiarum degree in palaeontology and historical geology, and has worked in Mesozoic and Cenozoic palynology at the Norwegian Petroleum Directorate since 1985.

Ma	Period	Era
	Quaternary	Cenozoic
	Neogene	
50	Palaeogene	
100	Cretaceous	Mesozoic
150	Jurassic	
200	Triassic	
250	Permian	Palaeozoic
300	Carboniferous	
350	Devonian	
400	Silurian	
450	Ordovician	
500	Cambrian	
550	Ediacaran	Neo-proterozoic
600		

Page numbers of places mentioned in the text.

133

Index

"A marvellous little book, full of nuggets of wisdom from the 'who's who?' of our industry. I highly recommend this book to all young and aspiring geoscientists."

Dan Hampson — co-founder of Hampson–Russell

"I liked the informal tone and the down-to-earth advice. The bite-sized pieces of advice will be most useful to students starting out in the field. It's a fundamental truth that it is way more efficient to progress in your discipline if you gaze at the horizon standing on the shoulders of those who came before..."

Henry Posamentier — seismic geomorphologist

Published November 2013

Available from *ageo.co/52geology*
& online bookstores worldwide.

$19 • £12 • €15

ISBN 978-0-9879594-2-3

"This new book is full of practical tips, commentary, and
advice from real geologists who have been there
and know what the science is all about."

Andrew D Miall — Professor of Geology, University of Toronto

"If you're right at the start of your career this volume will put
you in touch with the human side of a geoscientist's life in oil
and gas, and will entertain as well as enlighten you.
For anyone else, you may nevertheless enjoy the insights
into the preoccupations, predilections, and prejudices
of the life of an exploration geologist."

David E Smith — Professor of Geography, University of Oxford

14323874R00081

Printed in Poland
by Amazon Fulfillment
Poland Sp. z o.o., Wrocław